Could There Be Any More Trivia?

A quiz book about 'Friends'

Unofficial & Unauthorized

By Kylie Digges

D1365325

Kylie Digges

For Tim:
Thank you for being the Chandler to my Monica

Kylie Digges

Table of Contents

A note from the author

"Oh. My. God." "We were on a break!" "You're in the friend zone." "Joey doesn't share food!" "Smelly Cat." "They don't know that we know they know we know."

"Friends," the modern classic sitcom created by Marta Kauffman and David Crane that ran on NBC for 10 seasons, has been off the air since 2004. But thanks to syndicated reruns, DVD collections, streaming services, Buzzfeed quizzes and a multitude of internet GIFs of its endlessly quotable dialogue, it's never really left the pop culture zeitgeist.

But how well do you remember details from the show? This book is here to test you.

There are 63 chapters, each with 10 questions. There are two kinds of chapters:

1. Season-specific quizzes that increase in difficulty the farther into the book you go — you'll start with Season 1: Easy and finish with Season 10: Difficult.
2. Three varieties of themed quizzes: Categories, such as The One with All the Animals; Twosomes, which are quizzes about different pairings like Rachel and Phoebe or Chandler and Joey; and Relationships, which cover the dating life of each of the friends (when they're not dating each other, that is.) Themed quizzes have questions of varying difficulty from the whole run of the show.

At the end of each chapter is a Quotable. I'll give you a line or a few lines of dialogue, and you try to finish with the punchline. Sometimes harder than it seems…

On a personal note, my "Friends" obsession began early. In about 2000, I taped the whole show from syndication on VHS and then created dubbed versions with every episode — in order — to give as Christmas gifts. (Alas, the DVD sets were released about a year after I completed that project. I have since purchased all 10 sets. Sigh.)

I have a "Friends" poster right above my desk in my office. I immediately clear my schedule when there's a "Friends"-themed trivia night. Approximately 95% of all conversations I have with my brother involve an extended sequence of us quoting "Friends" lines at each other.

I love this show, and I loved writing this book. I hope you find these quizzes enjoyable, challenging and that it prompts a lot of laughs for you and your own friends.

Season 1: Easy

From Rachel running into Central Perk in a wedding dress to Ross getting off a plane with Julie: Try these basic questions about Season 1.

1. Who is the girls' downstairs neighbor who always complains about the noise they make?

2. In what type of food does Rachel lose her engagement ring from Barry?

3. What is Phoebe's twin sister's name?

4. What's the name of the East German laundry detergent Ross gets for his laundry date with Rachel?

5. What actor is Joey hired to act as a butt double for, only to be fired because he "acted too much with it"?

6. Chandler's mom says during her "Tonight Show" interview that she always likes to eat what dish after she's been intimate with a man?

7. What "Pennsylvania Dutch" name does Monica give Fake Monica when they meet in person?

8. What Scrabble tiles does Marcel swallow, prompting Ross to rush him to the hospital?

9. What Macy's Thanksgiving Day Parade balloon escapes, causing the friends to rush to the roof to see it fly over the city untethered?

10. What musical that has an exclamation point in the title — much to Phoebe's dismay — does Joey star in?

Quotables:
Ross: Have you never done this before?
Rachel: Well, not myself, but I know other people that have. OK, you caught me. I'm a laundry virgin.
Ross: Uh, well, don't worry. ... *What comes next?*

Answers on page 137.

Ross and Rachel

Over 10 seasons, these two took us on quite a roller coaster ride of emotions. How well do you remember their ups and downs?

1. Who says "I love you" first, Ross or Rachel?

2. What's written on the tiny T-shirt that Ross demands back from Rachel, saying it's missing from the box of his stuff that she gives him after they break up?

3. Where does Ross say he eventually was planning to propose to Rachel, if they had never broken up?

4. What five negative things does Ross put on the con side for Rachel when he makes the list to decide between her and Julie?

5. Where do Ross and Rachel have their very first kiss?

6. In Season 9, Ross and Rachel have a big fight that leads to them deciding they shouldn't live together anymore. What is Ross mad about?

7. How many pages is the letter that Rachel writes to Ross while he is breaking up with Bonnie?

8. What does Rachel call a one-time-only, no-strings-attached hookup between two exes, such as the one she suggests to Ross in Season 7?

9. Who is the first to know the sex of their baby, Ross or Rachel?

10. Where was Ross and Rachel's Las Vegas wedding dinner?

Quotables:
Rachel: In the future, when a girl asks for some ill-advised sympathy sex... just do it.
Ross: Wait, wait — You're mad at me about last night? I was just trying to do the right thing.
Rachel: Really? Well, it seems to me if you'd done the right thing, I would not have woken up today feeling stupid and embarrassed, I would have... *What comes next?*

Answers on page 137.

Season 2: Easy

Joey becomes a soap opera star, Monica falls in love with a much older, mustachioed man and Rachel realizes Ross is her lobster. Give these simple questions from the sophomore season a go.

1. What is the first episode to feature "Fat Monica"?

2. What does Joey call the technique where he pauses and looks really intense while trying to remember his next line of dialogue?

3. What's the name of the Central Perk manager who's in love with Rachel?

4. What song does Phoebe get "discovered" for that leads to a demo and a video – though she finds out her voice is dubbed?

5. What character does Joey play on "Days of Our Lives"?

6. What is Jack Geller's nickname for Monica?

7. When they start hanging out, what does Chandler do to emulate Richard?

8. What does Rachel claim was the reason for her nose job?

9. What did Monica's parents do with her childhood bedroom after she moved out?

10. After Joey gets his own place, what new roommate — who is revealed to be a bit unhinged — moves in with Chandler?

Quotables:
Ross: You, uh, you don't believe in gravity?
Phoebe: Well, it's not so much that, you know, like I don't believe in it, you know, it's just... I don't know. Lately I get the feeling that I'm not so much being pulled down as I am being pushed.
[Someone knocks on the door]
Chandler: Uh-oh. ... *What comes next?*

Answers on page 138.

The One with All the Animals

Monkeys, farm birds and a cat that looks like a hand: The friends certainly shared a lot of screen time with members of the animal kingdom. Can you answer these calls of the wild?

1. Whose cat attacks Ross on the balcony during the blackout while Monica, Phoebe and Joey sing, happily unaware, in the living room?

2. When Ross is planning to get a cat with Julie, he picks up old cat toys from Monica that belonged to what former cat of hers?

3. What two names do Chandler and Joey come up with for the hypothetical offspring of the chick and the duck?

4. What does Rachel call the cat she briefly owns (before she unloads it on Gunther)?

5. What is the name of the hamster that belongs to Cheryl, the girl with the incredibly messy apartment who Ross dates?

6. What was the name of the dog that Ross believed actually did go "to live upstate" on the Milners' farm?

7. What's the real name of the cat Phoebe finds that she thinks is her mother reincarnated?

8. Why does Ross claim he got hurt while playing badminton with Rachel's dad?

9. When one of Mike's groomsmen can't make the wedding, Phoebe assigns Rachel the bridesmaid job of choosing between Ross and Chandler for the spot, but it ends up going to what Hannigan family pet?

10. What baby animals does Phoebe adopt, much to the group's horror, after Mike kills their parent?

Quotables:
Phoebe: Turkeys are beautiful, intelligent animals!
Joey: No, they're not! ... *What comes next?*

Answers on page 138.

Season 3: Easy

Season 3 had a lot more going on than just Ross and Rachel's heart-wrenching breakup. How well do you remember it?

1. Which of Joey's sisters does a drunken Chandler fool around with at a party?

2. After she tells him she's not going, what does Ross agree to do to prove how much he wants Rachel to attend the museum benefit?

3. What kind of bed is accidentally delivered to Monica?

4. Who does Ross sleep with while he and Rachel are "on a break"?

5. What toy that they use for messages do Joey and Chandler have hanging on the inside of the door to their apartment?

6. Where does Phoebe's biological mother live?

7. What is the primary building material for the giant poking device?

8. What does Janice call the day out she has with Joey for them to try to bond for Chandler's sake?

9. What is the Geller Cup made out of?

10. What does Joey do when a book scares him?

Quotables:

Monica: Monica bang! Everybody bang! Ben bang! Rachel bang! Bang, Rachel! Bang!

[Rachel and Monica knock their heads on the beam]

Rachel: OK, I'm stopping now. Oh, yeah. You know... *What comes next?*

Answers on page 139.

Joey and Chandler

Hug it out with these questions about our favorite pair of bros, J-Man and Channy.

1. After they are robbed of all their furniture except the entertainment unit, Joey and Chandler trade it for what item?

2. According to Chandler, what kind of candy is Joey always leaving around the apartment?

3. What's engraved on the gold bracelet that Joey gives Chandler?

4. What game involving tennis balls, oven mitts and lighter fluid do Joey and Chandler invent?

5. What is Joey's explanation for why Chandler can't cry?

6. After getting in a fight over Joey not washing silverware, what does Chandler buy him to try to make amends?

7. What item from their apartment does Joey give Chandler as a going-away present when Chandler leaves their place to move in with Monica?

8. What does Chandler do at Joey's movie premiere to anger Joey?

9. When he's moving out, Chandler invents what game in order to give money to Joey, who's too proud to accept a loan to cover his expenses?

10. How long does Joey sentence Chandler to staying in the box in order to forgive him for kissing Kathy?

Quotables:
Joey: Why don't you go see Frankie? My family's been going to him forever. He did my first suit when I was 15. No, wait, 16. No, excuse me, 15. All right, when was 1990?
Chandler: OK, you have to… *What comes next?*

Answers on page 139.

Season 4: Easy

Travel time: We start at the beach and end up in London. Answer these easy questions about Season 4.

1. Who gets stung by a jellyfish at the beach?

2. What volume of encyclopedia does Joey buy from a door-to-door salesman?

3. How many categories does Monica have for her towels?

4. Apart from Ross saying the wrong name at his wedding, what other surprise twist happens in the Season 4 finale?

5. What are Frank Jr. and Alice's triplets named?

6. What's Joey's famous pick-up line?

7. What does Rachel say happened when a misunderstanding led to her wearing a negligee as a dress to dinner with Joshua's parents?

8. Where does Chandler tell Janice he has to move for work to avoid getting back together with her?

9. What does Rachel yell at Ross as he's angrily leaving her apartment after their second breakup that prompts Chandler to shout, "I knew it!"?

10. Which woman who Chandler dates handcuffs him to her office chair as an element of foreplay?

Quotables:
Joey: Man, it is so hard to shop for girls.
Chandler: Yes, it is at... *What comes next?*

Answers on page 140.

Romancing Rachel

Rachel had a lively love life in between leaving Barry at the altar and getting back with Ross for good. How many of these guys can you recall?

1. What Italian hunk does Rachel meet during the blackout?

2. In a bid to get to kiss Joshua, what game does Rachel suggest they play at the fake going away party for Emily?

3. Name Rachel's assistant who she secretly dates for a while.

4. What's the name of the obstetrician who Rachel flirts with at the hospital while Carol is in labor?

5. Who is the new neighbor in the building who the girls first call the yeti and who Rachel briefly dates?

6. Out of spite, Monica spills the beans on the phone to Rachel's father that Rachel had sex with who on her dad's bed during high school?

7. Which "Days of Our Lives" co-star of Joey's does Rachel date while she's pregnant, upsetting Ross?

8. When Rachel asks Paul to open up about himself and tell her something from his childhood, what traumatic nickname does he share that causes him to start sobbing?

9. Who is Rachel on a date with when she gets drunk and calls Ross to tell him she's over him and get "closure"?

10. What's the name of the guy Rachel dates who turns out to be an angry screamer, yelling at Ross, strangers and even the chick?

Quotables:
Ross: So, the first time you asked a guy out, he turned you down?
Rachel: He didn't turn me down. He's at the game, isn't he?
… What comes next?

Answers on page 140.

Season 5: Easy

Ross wears leather pants, Joey gets his "big break" and everybody finds out about Monica and Chandler. Time for some simple queries about Season 5.

1. Who is Joey's bedtime penguin pal?

2. When they're putting together Rachel's surprise birthday party, Monica takes over all the planning and leaves Phoebe in charge of what two things?

3. What word does Ross famously bellow while trying to get his couch up the stairs of his apartment building?

4. Why is Chandler initially not allowed to join the marathon game of catch?

5. What does Ross draw on Rachel's face while she's asleep on the plane to Vegas?

6. What new couple does Monica feel threatened by when she realizes she and Chandler are no longer in the "can't keep their hands off each other" phase of their relationship?

7. What condition does Emily give Ross when she finally agrees to move to New York to work on their marriage?

8. Where is Phoebe when she learns of Monica and Chandler's relationship?

9. What annoying device does Ross bring with him when he moves in to Joey and Chandler's that Chandler recognizes from when they were college roommates?

10. When Monica puts a turkey on her head to apologize to Chandler about his severed pinky toe, what two additional items does she add to the look?

Quotables:
Ross: Y'know what? I'm gonna go out on a limb and say no divorces in '99!
Rachel: But your divorce isn't even final yet.
Ross: ... *What comes next?*

Answers on page 141.

Monica and Phoebe

Try your hand at these questions about the former roommates; they are neither high maintenance nor floopy.

1. Who did Phoebe sleep with an hour after he had broken up with Monica?

2. Monica and Phoebe try waxing their legs with what supposed miracle product?

3. Which of Monica's restaurants does Phoebe play her guitar outside of, causing a fight between her and Monica over how classy and/or pretentious the place is?

4. What does Monica ask for from Phoebe as an engagement present?

5. What business did Monica and Phoebe briefly have together?

6. When Phoebe agrees to cut Monica's hair, what actor does she accidentally style Mon's new look after?

7. Monica and Phoebe face off as superheroes at the Halloween party. Who are they dressed as?

8. What three items does Phoebe bring to play with Monica's dollhouse that Monica doesn't approve of?

9. Why does Phoebe stop giving Monica massages?

10. After Phoebe and Mike break up, Monica is trying to prevent her from calling him so she decides to take Phoebe's cell phone away. How does Monica get it from her?

Quotables:
Monica: I can cook and you can take care of the money.
Phoebe: Ooh! ... *What comes next?*

Answers on page 141.

Season 6: Easy

Answer these basic questions about the only season apart from the finale that doesn't end with a cliffhanger.

1. What furniture store does Rachel purchase a new table from, though she has to conceal its origins from Phoebe?

2. What does Ross call the "total state of awareness" that he learned in karate class?

3. What kind of car does Joey find the keys to at Central Perk?

4. When Monica and Chandler are moving in together, Phoebe says Rachel can't live with her because she already has a roommate named what?

5. Which friend's apartment is partly destroyed by a fire?

6. What does Joey commit to buy at a silent auction, because he doesn't know how silent auctions work?

7. At what college does Ross get a job as a lecturer?

8. What item of Chandler's does Monica not want him to move in, setting off a huge fight about how Monica thinks of it as her apartment where nothing is Chandler's?

9. Because the pages of her cookbook are stuck together, Rachel makes a mashup of what two recipes for her Thanksgiving dessert?

10. Which friend isn't there for the group hug after Chandler and Monica get engaged?

Quotables:
Joey: You didn't cry when Bambi's mother died?
Chandler: Yes, it was very sad when... *What comes next?*

Answers on page 141.

The One with All the Siblings

Try these questions about brothers and sisters on for size. (And we're not counting Ross and Monica – they get their own chapter later.)

1. How many sisters does Joey have?

2. What does Jill tell Rachel that she did to cause her father to cut her off financially?

3. Frank Jr. shows up for the last time in Season 10 to ask Phoebe to do what (though he changes his mind during the course of the episode)?

4. What does Amy do while babysitting Emma that infuriates Ross and Rachel?

5. What does Jill say is the only thing she can't have?

6. What's the name of the guy that Joey wants to force his pregnant sister to marry?

7. What did Ursula do with Phoebe's birth certificate?

8. How does Joey describe Amy?

9. What souvenir does Frank Jr. want to pick up from Times Square while he's in New York visiting Phoebe for the first time?

33

10. What distinguishing feature does Rachel notice that proves it's Ursula, not Phoebe, appearing in porn videos?

Quotables:
Frank Jr.: You just don't know how hard it is, Phoebe. There's just so many of 'em. You know, two I can handle. Two's great. You just hold one in each hand. But what do I do when the third one runs at me with his bike helmet on? I've got no more hands to protect my area! There's three of them, Phoebe. Three!
Phoebe: Yeah, I know, Frank. ... *What comes next?*

Answers on page 142.

Season 7: Easy

Answer painless questions about the season that could collectively be called, "The One Where Monica and Chandler Plan Their Wedding."

1. What is the "truth about London"?

2. What is Joey's chair named?

3. What does Ross dress up as in order to teach Ben about Hanukkah?

4. What alarming fact does Phoebe learn on her 30th birthday?

5. Who are the nap partners?

6. Which character got glasses in Season 7 because the actor actually needed to start wearing them?

7. What was Rachel's sorority nickname, according to her old friend Melissa?

8. What instrument does Ross try to learn how to play as a special treat for Monica and Chandler's wedding?

9. What did Jack and Judy spend Monica's wedding fund on?

10. Which two friends get stuck on the roof together?

Quotables:

Monica: This is the most special day of our lives.

Chandler: I realize that, honey, but I'm not going to spend all the money on one party.

Monica: Honey, I love you. But, um, if you call our wedding a party one more time… *What comes next?*

Answers on page 142.

Ross and Monica

Despite their penchant for revealing embarrassing secrets from each other's pasts to people, Ross and Monica are most definitely #siblinggoals. How well do you know them?

1. What do Ross and Monica call the choreographed junior high talent show dance they bust out at the taping of "Dick Clark's New Year's Rockin' Eve?

2. What quirky travel habit, inherited from their mom, do Ross and Monica both do?

3. Ross claims he got a 1450 on his SATs. Monica makes sure everyone knows he actually got what?

4. In what year of the Geller Bowl game did Monica accidentally break Ross' nose?

5. What's the name of Ross and Monica's childhood pediatrician?

6. When Ross and Monica are fighting over what to watch on TV, Monica wants to watch "Entertainment Tonight." What does Ross want to watch?

7. What does Ross call the gravy-soaked piece of bread in Monica's Thanksgiving leftovers sandwiches?

8. What's the title of Ross and Monica's family newsletter?

9. When Monica and Ross alternate spilling secrets to their parents at Thanksgiving, what are the five secrets?

10. Neither Ross nor Monica handled turning 30 very well. What did they each do?

Quotables:
Monica: All right, but I'm very excited about this, OK? So, promise you won't get big-brothery and judgmental.
Ross: I promise. What?
Monica: It's Richard Burke.
Ross: Who's Richard Burke? Dr. Burke? You have a date with Dr. Burke? Why? Why? Why should that bother me? ... *What comes next?*

Answers on page 143.

Season 8: Easy

Rachel's pregnancy dominated Season 8, and Jennifer Aniston won an Emmy for the episode where she gives birth. Hopefully you won't have to labor too hard on these Season 8 questions.

1. What's Chandler's middle name?

2. What item of clothing is the key to the gang solving the mystery of who fathered Rachel's baby?

3. Ross tries to tell Mona he's not ready to send out a joint holiday card, but panics when she asks where the relationship is going and ends up offering her what?

4. Who is the fifth woman to share Rachel's birthing room?

5. What does Chandler take in the bubble bath with him to feel more masculine?

6. Joey enlists Chandler and Ross to help him practice when he has an audition to be the host of what game show?

7. What incredibly expensive item of clothing does Monica buy and promise to wear all the time to make up for the cost?

8. Who do Monica and Phoebe forget to invite to Rachel's baby shower?

9. What does Judy give to Ross at the hospital while Rachel is in labor?

10. What's the fake name that Joey sometimes gives to women he's hitting on?

Quotables:
Chandler: I know it's tough now, but things will get better.
Rachel: How do you know that? What if it just gets worse and worse and worse, to the point where we can't even be in the same room with each other?
Chandler: I'm not great at the advice. ... *What comes next?*

Answers on page 144.

The One with All the Travel

Road trip! How much do you recall about the episodes and plotlines that venture outside the Village?

1. Where does Monica's hair go bananas due to the humidity?

2. What phrase does Joey keep repeating, driving Chandler nuts, when they go to England for Ross' wedding?

3. Before she misses her flight, Rachel is planning to go to what ski resort city with her family for Thanksgiving?

4. In order to make Phoebe feel better about missing London, the friends all are heading to what vacation destination when her water breaks?

5. To what state do Joey and Monica drive to get Powerball tickets for the group when the jackpot reaches $300 million?

6. Where were Ross and Emily planning to take their honeymoon?

7. What's the occasion for Monica getting her and Chandler tickets to Las Vegas?

8. Where does David the Scientist Guy's grant take him for his research?

9. Where were Barry and Rachel supposed to go on their honeymoon (which he actually ended up going on with Mindy)?

10. In what New York hamlet do Ross, Monica and the gang celebrate Jack and Judy's 35th anniversary?

Quotables:
Phoebe: So, so far is this trip to Vegas better or worse than the trip to London?
Chandler: So far, it's pretty much the same, Pheebs.
Phoebe: OK, what about after… *What comes next?*

Answers on page 144.

Season 9: Easy

Rachel and Ross are new parents, Monica and Chandler try for a baby and Phoebe meets "The One." All this and a paleontology conference!

1. Rachel has a dream in Season 9 that sets off a major crush on whom?

2. Who accidentally breaks all of Monica and Chandler's wedding china?

3. What is Ross and Rachel's daughter's full name?

4. How does Joey know Mike before he introduces him to Phoebe on their double blind date?

5. What's the name of the co-worker of Chandler's in Tulsa who hits on him when he's stuck there for Christmas?

6. Who does Ross invite to the soap opera party, though she ends up kissing Joey?

7. What is the name of the male nanny that Ross has such a problem with?

8. What game do Mike and Monica play in Barbados?

9. Who drops the bowl of all the lottery tickets off the balcony?

10. Why does Monica get so much applause at Mike's karaoke bar?

Quotables:
Phoebe: Wow, Joey and a professor! Can you imagine if they had kids, and if the kids got her intelligence and Joey's raw sexual magnetism? ... *What comes next?*

Answers on page 144.

Rachel and Chandler

What can compete with the bond formed through parental divorce, handcuff secrets and cheesecake larceny? Here's a quiz about Rachel and Chandler.

1. What shop makes the irresistible cheesecakes that Rachel and Chandler inadvertently steal from a neighbor and end up fighting over?

2. What item does Rachel demand back from Chandler in exchange for unlocking him from the handcuffs?

3. What does Chandler give Rachel for her birthday in Season 1?

4. What guy from his office does Chandler set Rachel up with, but he makes the mistake of telling him that she's only looking for a fling?

5. What does the birthday card (which was intended to be a joke) that Chandler gives to Rachel on her 30th birthday say that makes her cry?

6. When she's sick of waitressing, what does Chandler tell Rachel she needs in order to find a new job?

7. When she's leaving for Paris, what does Chandler hide from Rachel as a joke, leading to her starting to rip open all her carefully packed boxes and bags?

8. Chandler tells Rachel he got through his parents' divorce with a carefully regimented program of denial and what?

9. What song starts playing when Rachel hits the jukebox in her flashback fantasy about making out with Chandler?

10. What TV show's cancellation does Chandler compare Rachel's moving away with?

Quotables:
Chandler: I don't wanna know what Monica got me. Y'know? I mean, look, I'm sure she worked really hard at getting me a present and wanting to surprise me, and you guys are gonna ruin that, and … Look we have to put these back; this is not what Christmas is about.
Rachel: … *What comes next?*

Answers on page 145.

Season 10: Easy

Major changes abound in the final, emotional season. Ease into the feels with these easy questions.

1. What language does Phoebe try to teach Joey for an audition, but all he can say is gibberish words?

2. What long-running character dies in Season 10?

3. What playground apparatus is Rachel deathly afraid of, so she won't let Emma near them?

4. What game show does Joey appear on as a celebrity contestant?

5. What outlandish name does Phoebe briefly give herself legally after she marries Mike?

6. Why are Phoebe and Rachel late to Thanksgiving?

7. What do Monica and Chandler name their twins?

8. After Ross confesses his love at the airport gate, Rachel boards anyway. What does she later say when he looks up and sees her standing in his doorway?

9. What's the final line of the series and who says it?

10. What item is in the final shot of the final episode of "Friends"?

Quotables:
Ross: Oh, my God!
Monica: You were my midnight mystery kisser?
Ross: You were my first kiss with Rachel?
Monica: You were my first kiss ever?
Chandler: ... *What comes next?*

Answers on page 145.

Ross' Relationships

Sure, Ross' trajectory was all about Rachel for a decade, but when they were off, he was no slouch in the dating game. Answer these questions about Ross, "The Divorcer."

1. What state do Ross and Emily end up in on their first date?

2. What does Mona bring Ross as a souvenir from her trip to Atlantic City?

3. What ride did Ross and Carol have sex on at Disneyland, causing them to be banned from the park?

4. What's the name of the pizza delivery girl that Ross tries unsuccessfully to flirt with?

5. Where did Ross and Julie first meet?

6. Ross meets a great woman on the train and starts dating her, but it's a semi-long distance relationship because she's from what city in New York?

7. What's the name of the "bug lady," or insect curator, who Ross goes out with and tries to talk dirty to?

8. Ross wears his leather pants on a date with what unusually named woman?

9. What was Ross' nickname for Elizabeth before he knew her name and she was just a student in one of his big lecture classes?

10. Why do Ross and Charlie break up?

Quotables:
Rachel: Oh, hey, Ross... Listen, I heard about you and Charlie. I'm really sorry.
Ross: Oh, that's OK. I'm sure there are tons of other beautiful paleontologists out there.
Rachel: Absolutely.
Ross: There was one! She's it! All the rest... *What comes next?*

Answers on page 146.

Season 1: Hard

Take another trip back in time to the 1994-1995 season. Things get tougher now...

1. Monica says the first line on the first episode. What is it?

2. What does Ross call Marcel's "safety zoo"?

3. Who is Joey's Valentine's Day date who brings her friend, Janice, to be Chandler's date?

4. Who did Monica agree to make a dozen lasagnas for?

5. What's the name of the homeless woman who Phoebe gives away her bank error money to?

6. What does Monica call the rum blender drink she makes for the girls' slumber party?

7. When Joey does a modeling gig for the Free Clinic and ends up on a poster for VD, what name is on the poster?

8. What three things are on Chandler's alternative-to-Thanksgiving menu?

9. When Barry has his romance with Rachel while engaged to Mindy, where does he take her for lunch?

10. What does WENUS stand for?

Quotables:

Rachel: So basically, you get your ya-yas by taking money from all of your friends.

Ross: … Yeah.

Chandler: Yes, and I get my ya-yas from Ikea. … *What comes next?*

Answers on page 146.

Joey and Phoebe

Our favorite oddballs of the group had a special bond, though it was never romantic. Try this quiz about Joseph Francis and Pheebs.

1. Phoebe doesn't know the actual guitar chord names, so she named them based on how her hand looks when she's doing them. When she is teaching Joey to play, which six does she mention?

2. What does Phoebe tell Joey is the reason he doesn't have any past life memories?

3. While Joey is answering phones at the PBS telethon, what is Phoebe trying to find an example of to prove him wrong about an argument they had?

4. What's the name of the casting director that Phoebe first calls while pretending to be Joey's agent?

5. Phoebe and Joey get together for dinner once a month to do what?

6. What does Joey tell Phoebe his physical assessment of her when they first met was?

7. What two food items does Joey have in the shower with him when Phoebe comes in to sniff out a pregnancy craving smell?

8. What does Phoebe say about Joey that gets the interviewer from "Soap Opera Digest" to want to quote her?

9. Joey gets Phoebe a spot as an extra on "Days of Our Lives" when she's low on money. What's the first "role" she plays?

10. Phoebe and Joey kiss five times throughout the course of the show, though never truly romantically. Describe the scenarios that led to those kisses.

Quotables:
Joey: What if I said I could even things out for you, meat-wise?
Phoebe: What?
Joey: Well, I eat a lot of meat, right? But suppose, until the baby's born, I laid off it. No extra animals would die; you'd just be eating my animals.
Phoebe: Joey, I can't believe you would do that for me.
Joey: Absolutely! I could be a vegetarian. ... *What comes next?*

Answers on page 147.

Season 2: Hard

Hootie and the Blowfish, a lesbian wedding, chicken pox and more. Give these hard questions about Season 2 a go.

1. After giving him up in Season 1, Ross sees his monkey, Marcel, again in a television commercial for what product?

2. According to Chandler, what's the next stop after Bittertown and Aloneville?

3. What term do Judy and her friends use when they're talking about Richard's new young girlfriend, not knowing they're talking about Monica?

4. What is Joey's nickname for his genitalia?

5. Who was Monica's date to the prom?

6. What's was the name of Gunther's soap opera character on "All My Children," and how was he killed off?

7. After he sprays cologne in a customer's eye, it's revealed that the Hombre Man's real name is what?

8. What's the name of the self-empowerment book that Rachel, Monica and Phoebe become obsessed with?

9. What did Mr. Heckles title the journal where he kept a list of his complaints about his neighbors?

10. What three things is Ross allergic to?

Quotables:
Chandler: Your little men are gonna get scored on more times than your sister.
Joey: Whoa, whoa, whoa, WHOA! ... *What comes next?*

Answers on page 148.

The One with All the Weddings

Some of these don't even involve Ross! Say "I do" to questions about weddings on "Friends."

1. What off-the-beaten-path color is Phoebe's wedding dress?

2. Despite taking lessons to surprise Monica, why can't Chandler dance at his wedding?

3. Which cousin of Ross and Monica's gets married and only invites Ross, so Monica forces him to take her as his guest so she can confront the bride about the snub?

4. What religion is the minister that Rachel finds to perform Monica and Chandler's wedding in case Joey can't get there?

5. Who walks Carol down the aisle at her wedding?

6. What instrument does Phoebe's friend Marjorie play at her wedding?

7. What song does Rachel sing at Barry and Mindy's wedding?

8. What are the names of the three young girls that Ross dances with at Monica and Chandler's wedding in order to gain points with Mona?

9. Why do Ross and Emily choose a wedding date only four weeks after their engagement?

10. How many people were on the guest list for Monica and Chandler's wedding?

Quotables:
Rachel: You know what, Barr? I'm not going to leave. I probably should, but I'm not. See, 'cause I promised myself I would make it through at least one of your weddings. See now, tonight, all I really wanted was to make it through this evening with a little bit of grace and dignity. ... *What comes next?*

Answers on page 148.

Season 3: Hard

Joey and Chandler become parents to a chick and a duck, Rachel does get the hair wrong on Ross' fantasy role play and Phoebe reminds us that you NEVER run on a barge. Harder questions about Season 3: Get to it!

1. What is the name of the denim fashion label that made Joey's quite-snug "work pants"?

2. Name Phoebe's ex-singing partner who encourages Phoebe to sell her songs as commercial jingles.

3. What are the original lineups of the touch football game teams?

4. What play is Joey starring in when he falls for his co-star Kate?

5. According to Ross, what are the three P's of championship tennis play?

6. What's the name of the ubiquitous software program that Pete's company makes?

7. What condition does Chandler warn Ross he's going to get while Ross is at Chandler's place obsessively watching for Rachel to come back from her date with Mark?

8. What food item gets spilled on Phoebe's dress when Chandler and Joey are fighting over the chair instead of getting ready?

9. What is the name of Rachel's chiropractor?

10. What celebrity name does Ross use to book a restaurant reservation? (In a funny twist, that celebrity ended up guest-starring on the show several seasons later.)

Quotables:
Ross: Hey, Joey. Are men ever nice to strange women for no reason?
Joey: ... *What comes next?*

Answers on page 149.

Rachel and Monica

High school besties who drifted apart but grew closer than ever when they became unexpected roommates years later. Gotta love it. How well do you know Monica and Rachel?

1. Why is Rachel not allowed to borrow Monica's stuff?

2. In junior high, Rachel left a Valentine in Monica's locker that she pretended was from whom?

3. When does Monica catch on to the fact that Rachel is pregnant, not Phoebe?

4. What action star do Rachel and Monica meet on the set on Marcel's movie and end up fighting over?

5. What tacky item from Mr. Heckles' apartment does Rachel love and Monica accidentally break?

6. What kitchen appliance are Rachel and Monica looking for in the basement storage room when they meet the Yeti and fog him?

7. To convince Phoebe to move in with Rachel, Monica mentions four nice things Rachel does as a roommate – what are they?

8. Rachel is hurt and offended when Monica hires which waitress from her restaurant to work at her job audition dinner?

9. What four things are on the menu of the meal that Monica cooks so that Rachel can pretend that she made it for her date with Joshua?

10. What do Monica and Rachel do to finally get their apartment back once and for all?

Quotables:
Monica: Look, you and I went to different high schools...
Rachel: OK, that doesn't help me, because we went to the same high school.
Monica: You went to one where you were popular, and you got to ride off on Chip's motorcycle and wear his letterman jacket. I went to one where I wore a band uniform they had to have specially made.
Rachel: They had to have that specially made?
Monica: It was a project for one of the Home Ec. classes.
Rachel: Oh, my God... *What comes next?*

Answers on page 149.

Season 4: Hard

Challenge yourself with this tough quiz about the season where Ross gets his ear pierced, Joey dances with Treeger and Chandler crosses the line.

1. What gifts that Phoebe can use after she's done being pregnant do Rachel and Monica get her for her baby shower?

2. What is Joey's definition of Phase 3 of a breakup?

3. What three-word term does Ross ask that the gang think of his songs as?

4. Joey's reasons for Chandler being in the box are threefold: What are they?

5. Name the actress who plays Emily.

6. What is Monica's quirk about Tic-Tacs?

7. What three mementoes does Rachel produce to prove to Ross that even though she exchanges gifts, she still has sentiment about the things that matter?

8. In the trivia game Ross writes for the "Who knows who best?" game, what are the four categories?

9. What chocolate bar is in Emily's bag while she's on the phone with Ross, enticing Joey?

10. Where did Phoebe get the maternity wedding dress she wears when the girls decide to hang out in bridal attire?

Quotables:

Phoebe: Hey, can we put on the news? I think it might be raining.

Ross: Just hold on a sec. I'm watching this rugby thing on ESPN. I don't know what the big deal is; I'm man enough to play this sport!

Joey: Dude, you're not even man enough to... *What comes next?*

Answers on page 150.

The One with All the Porn

For a show that aired in primetime, the writers sure liked to work in plotlines about porn. Give these questions a shot, even if you think the dialogue is corny and you find it funny, not sexy.

1. Who tells Joey and Chandler not to turn their TV off for fear of losing their free porn?

2. What four parody porn titles are mentioned as movies that Ursula has starred in using Phoebe's name?

3. Early in his career, Joey appeared in a porno movie as a guy trying to fix a copier, but two people are having sex on it. What was his line?

4. Monica surprises Chandler in Tulsa and mistakenly thinks she catches him engaging in what kind of fetish porn?

5. What porno does Joey order in Rachel and Phoebe's hotel room the night of Monica and Chandler's wedding?

6. What porn theme song does Rachel get stuck in her head while the guys have free porn on their TV?

7. When Monica suggests Chandler send a gift to Joey in Las Vegas to apologize for not believing in his big break, what does Chandler first think of?

8. In the alternate universe of The One That Could Have Been, Ross and Rachel run into each other for the first time in 13 years at a newsstand where Ross (who's sexually frustrated in his marriage to Carol) is buying a copy of what porn magazine?

9. Chandler and Ross fight over authorship of a joke published in what periodical?

10. Chandler, thinking it's a porn, watches and is horrified by a birthing video that Phoebe's friend loaned her to show to a pregnant Rachel. What's the video's misleadingly porny-sounding label on the tape?

Quotables:
Rachel: Hey, y'know what? I don't care! I'm not ashamed of my book. There's nothing wrong with a woman enjoying a little ... erotica. It's just a healthy expression of female sexuality, which by the way, you will never understand.
Joey: ... *What comes next?*

Answers on page 150.

Season 5: Hard

Rachel smokes, Ross moves in and a girl hits Joey: Put on your thinking cap for this hard Season 5 quiz.

1. Why did Rachel change her major during her freshman year of college?

2. What adjective does Phoebe use to describe herself when she tells Chandler he should be excited about having sex with her?

3. What two things does Joey say he is thankful for when the gang is sitting around after Thanksgiving dinner in Season 5?

4. What was the name of the cab driver in London who took the gang to The Wheatsheaf pub?

5. What two clues about Monica and Chandler's weekend away together does Joey put together to finally discover they're in a secret relationship?

6. How much is Joey getting paid for his "big break" movie role?

7. In a bid to win her affections, what song — that he wrote — is Ross planning to play for Rachel at Thanksgiving 1987?

8. What two adjectives does Chandler use to describe the look of someone who has recently smoked?

9. What is the tasty treat the duck and the chick are competing to find first when Joey and Phoebe are betting on them?

10. While couch shopping, what two things does Ross tell Rachel he wants his couch to say?

Quotables:
Rachel: Oh, my God! Oh, my God, look at these pelts!
Monica: Don't get too attached; she's having it cremated.
Rachel: What? Phoebe, honey... honey, I know you're quirky and I get a big kick out of it — we all do, actually — but if you destroy a coat like this, I mean, that is like a crime against nature! Ugh, no... *What comes next?*

Answers on page 151.

Ross and Phoebe

From the moment she tried to cleanse his aura, we all knew these two were very different people, but that didn't stop them from being the best of friends. How much do you know about Ross and Phoebe?

1. What play on a Police song does Phoebe sing-yell at Ross to convince him to get her concert tickets using his connection through Ben's schoolmate, Sting's son Jack?

2. Ross and Phoebe simultaneously date a couple who are going through a divorce, and they unwittingly develop biases about them and start arguing. Eventually that couple decides to get back together and dumps Phoebe and Ross. Who were they dating?

3. Phoebe stays at Ross' apartment temporarily to give newly engaged Monica and Chandler some space. What does she do there that freaks Ross out?

4. What does Ross buy for Phoebe when he learns she never had one as a kid?

5. Phoebe can't remember why she's mad at Ross, so they play the fast answer game to figure it out. Even though they discover it happened in a dream, why was she mad?

6. What three items does Phoebe bring to Ross' new apartment as a housewarming gift?

7. What's the name of Phoebe's street friend who tries to rob Ross?

8. In Phoebe's prediction of the future, Monica and Chandler get rich but break up. Joey has beautiful kids with Rachel and Phoebe marries Chandler for the money, then Phoebe and Joey ditch Rachel and Chandler and hook up. What happens to Ross?

9. What paleontology article did Phoebe see on Ross's coffee table and memorize so she could bring it up in conversation with Charlie and freak him out?

10. What are the three reasons Phoebe cites at the handyman's retirement party for why she understands why none of Ross' neighbors like him?

Quotables:
Ross: Pheebs, I have studied evolution my entire adult life. OK, I can tell you, we have collected fossils from all over the world that actually show the evolution of different species, OK? You can literally see them evolving through time.
Phoebe: Really? You can actually see it?
Ross: You bet. In the U.S., China, Africa, all over.
Phoebe: See, I didn't know that.
Ross: Well, there you go.
Phoebe: Huh. So now, the real question is... *What comes next?*

Answers on page 151.

Season 6: Hard

Challenge yourself with this set of hard questions about the season where we learn Chandler can't cry, meet the first of Rachel's two sisters and shake our heads sadly at Ross dancing on MTV's Spring Break.

1. What does Phoebe say her tombstone is going to say?

2. What are the conditions that Joey puts in his newspaper ad when he's looking for a new roommate when Chandler moves out?

3. What does Ross say he did on his spring break in college?

4. What decoy present does Monica hide under the couch to mess with Rachel and Phoebe, knowing they'll be looking for their Christmas gifts?

5. What two suggestions does Joey offer when Chandler asks for Valentine's Day gift ideas?

6. When Rachel decides to try Phoebe's style of running, what does she crash into?

7. Monica tries to seduce Chandler even though she's sick. He refuses, wanting her to rest and stay under the covers instead. What action finally gets Chandler to cave?

8. What does Joey name his boat?

9. What item of Ross' does Jill destroy after he refuses her sexual advances?

10. What signature drink of Monica's does Chandler discover at Richard's apartment, giving him confirmation she was there?

Quotables:
Monica: Y'know, I only know of two surefire ways to shut a man up. And one of them is sex.
Rachel: What's the other one?
Monica: I don't know… *What comes next?*

Answers on page 152.

Joey Has a Date

He hooked up with so many women during the course of the show, it's hard to keep track. Bust out your little black book to answer these questions about Joey's love life.

1. What's the name of the understudy that Joey sleeps with even though he's in love with Kate?

2. Joey dates a diminutive girl named Katie who jokingly punches him in the arm so often that he wants to dump her. What '80s child star played her?

3. Joey dates his roommate, Australian dancer Janine, for a little while. What's her last name?

4. Which girlfriend of Joey's operates a fruit basket company?

5. Which bridesmaid at Ross' wedding to Emily does Joey hook up with at the rehearsal dinner?

6. Chandler says Joey's "breakfast adventure" with what woman is what caused their dining table to break?

7. What does Joey's Valentine's Day date order to-go from the restaurant after she tells Joey she wants to slather his body with stuff and lick it off?

8. Sleeping with what woman prompted Joey to promote his junk, if in nickname only?

9. What woman's affections do Joey and The Hombre Man compete for?

10. What's the name of the obsessed soap opera fan who tracks down Joey's real address and sends him 14 of her eyelashes?

Quotables:
Joey: Because you didn't give me advice! No! You gave me a pickup line! As soon as I told her I wanted to, y'know, build a foundation and be friends first, I suddenly — through no fault of my own — became irresistible to her! And her roommate!
Monica: What about the closeness?
Joey: *... What comes next?*

Answers on page 152.

Season 7: Hard

Chandler's dad makes an appearance, Joey gets a new brain on "Days of Our Lives" and Monica's thunder gets stolen: It's hard questions about Season 7.

1. What fake last names does Rachel give Monica and Chandler when she's asking the Greek Orthodox priest to officiate their wedding?

2. What highly qualified and professional woman did Rachel hire as her assistant at Ralph Lauren before she changes her mind when the hot young male interviewee returns to thank her for giving him a shot?

3. What is Chandler's father's drag queen name?

4. What's the name of the character that dies and gets her brain transplanted into Drake Ramoray's body on "Days of Our Lives"?

5. What painkiller does Phoebe take for a headache, only to be horrified when she learns about the possible side effects?

6. What's the make and model of the fancy chair that Rachel buys to replace Joey's broken chair?

7. What celebrity was the original wearer of the tuxedo that finally fits Chandler perfectly?

8. What Disneyland ride was Ross on his junior year when he pooped his pants after eating too many tacos?

9. What band did Monica have planned for her wedding when she was in sixth grade?

10. After the guys watch "Die Hard," Joey and Ross plan to watch it again right away, but Chandler bails, citing what reason?

Quotables:
Ross: I remember when she took me out on her dad's boat, she wouldn't let me help out at all.
Rachel: Excuse me, I wanted you to help, but you couldn't move your arms because you were wearing three life jackets.
Ross: *... What comes next?*

Answers on page 153.

Monica and Chandler

An unlikely couple turns into one of TV's most endearing and lasting relationships. We're not crying, you're crying. Answer these queries about Mon and Chan.

1. On Monica and Chandler's first weekend away together, she keeps requesting to switch hotel rooms while Chandler is trying to watch what on TV?

2. What sport are Monica and Chandler playing with his boss when Chandler suggests they let him win?

3. What couple do Monica and Chandler make friends with on their honeymoon, only to find out when they get back to New York that they fake-numbered them?

4. Who says "I love you" first, Monica or Chandler?

5. On the anniversary that Monica bought Chandler a $500 watch, what did he get her?

6. The day after they get married, Monica and Chandler both do things that require the other to forgive them. They end up calling it even and high-fiving. What did they each do?

7. When Monica thought she had brought Chandler's severed toe to the hospital, it turned out she actually brought what?

8. In Vegas, Chandler tells Monica that they'll get married that night if she rolls what combination of dice?

9. When Monica starts proposing to Chandler, she gets down on one knee and gets about half a sentence out before she starts crying and says what?

10. When Monica and Chandler agree to exchange homemade presents for Valentine's Day, they both forget, scramble last-minute and end up exchanging what?

Quotables:
Monica: Honey, listen. You have nothing to worry about with Jeffrey.
Chandler: Oh, yeah? Is he funnier than me?
Monica: Well, you're... you're different funny. I mean, you're more sarcastic and... well, he does... bits... and impressions... and... and limericks...
Chandler: I do limericks. Uh... There once was a man named Chandler... *What comes next?*

Answers on page 153.

Season 8: Hard

Did you know that Season 8 is the only one of the series to feature a Halloween episode? If you did, you'll probably ace these hard questions.

1. What candy does Ross have in his hand when he comes to the hospital while Rachel is having Braxton-Hicks contractions?

2. Despite 20 hours with a dialect coach, what does Joey's Southern accent actually sound like?

3. What's the name of the maid that Chandler hires as a surprise for Monica?

4. What color is the shirt that Ross stealthily tries to get back from Mona's apartment?

5. What's the name of the guy that Joey interviews while pretending to be a doctor to see if he's good enough to date Phoebe?

6. What were the two baby name options that Ross and Rachel had narrowed it down to, but Rachel decides after their daughter is born that neither is right?

7. What's the mountain mentioned in the backpacking through Western Europe story that Joey teaches Ross?

8. What did Chandler think the response to "I love you" was until he was 25?

9. Who is Monica on the phone with when she says, "Oh, my God! My ass is sweating!"

10. Who peed on the ice sculpture at Monica and Chandler's engagement party?

Quotables:
Ross: Uh, in her defense, she's right. I am stronger. I would destroy you.
Chandler: Oh, really? You think you're stronger? Why don't you prove it?
[Chandler pushes Ross]
Ross: Oh, I'll prove it! ... *What comes next?*

Answers on page 154.

The One with All the Jobs

They must have had some way to pay for those inordinately large Greenwich Village apartments, right? Go to work and answer these questions about the friends' employment.

1. What company does Rachel go to work for right after she quits Central Perk?

2. Ross gets excited about teaching an advanced class, but learns the building it's in is way across town from the class he teaches right before it. How does he solve that problem?

3. At what Las Vegas hotel does Joey start working so that he doesn't have to tell his friends his movie production shut down?

4. Monica writes a scathing restaurant review, prompting the owner to come to her apartment and complain, but he ends up offering her the head chef gig at what establishment?

5. At his advertising internship, Chandler impresses the higher ups with a pitch for a commercial for the flame sneakers with wheels that has what tagline?

6. Why does Phoebe get fired from her masseuse job in Season 4?

7. After being super excited about how her interview went, Rachel finds out during the group poker game that she didn't get hired as a fashion buyer for what company?

8. Who is the second friend to get a job at Central Perk?

9. What enthralling topic did Ross write a paper on that gets him the university guest lecture gig?

10. When interviewing for a vice president job, what word does Chandler have to restrain himself from making childish jokes about, only to mention it at the end and blow the interview?

Quotables:
Phoebe: But there's a whole table of mini muffin baskets. Which one did you send?
Ross: The small one.
Rachel: What?! You-you actually thought that basket was gonna get you the apartment?
Ross: Well, yeah! Someone sent us a basket at work once and people went crazy over those little muffins. It was the best day.
Chandler: ... *What comes next?*

Answers on page 154.

Season 9: Hard

No one proposes, Monica sings karaoke and Ross holds the world's weirdest memorial service. Hard questions from Season 9, coming at you!

1. What are the names of Sandy's puppets, the Snufflebumps?

2. During their fight about Phoebe singing outside Monica's restaurant, Phoebe accuses Monica of using what ingredient too much?

3. What's Emma's first word?

4. What does Mike call Ross' apartment when Rachel asks him to go back in so he can intercept her phone call from the guy at the bar?

5. According to Joey, what is the highest level of hotness?

6. What advertising slogan does Ross claim he invented?

7. What's the name of the pediatrician who Rachel constantly calls during the first few weeks after she brings the baby home?

8. What was Ross' recurring nightmare as a child?

9. Despite being a vegetarian, what meat does Phoebe try to eat at dinner with Mike's parents to make a good impression?

10. When Chandler puts on Ross' alumni page that he died, what was the cause of death?

Quotables:
Monica: Why the hell did you take her?
Joey: Because you two were having sex!
Monica: No, we weren't!
Joey: Don't you lie to me! I can tell by Chandler's hair. …
What comes next?

Answers on page 155.

Chandler and Phoebe

These might be tricky; Phoebe and Chandler are the least common pairing of all our twosomes. Though they rarely had major storylines together, the ones they did were pretty memorable.

1. After she helps him prepare, what's Phoebe's final advice to Chandler as he heads to his big job interview?

2. How much does Chandler give Phoebe as a "deposit" for her to play guitar at his and Monica's wedding — but mainly to make her stop playing outside their bedroom door?

3. When Phoebe is in charge of guarding the engagement ring Chandler wants to buy, she tries on a boatload of jewelry and tiaras and gets distracted by holding what unusual final item while someone buys Chandler's ring?

4. What does Chandler invite Phoebe over to do, starting their game of sexual chicken?

5. The correct pronunciation of what superhero's name is once a hot topic of debate for Chandler and Phoebe?

6. Chandler and Phoebe agree to break up with their respective significant others at the same time for moral support. Who are they breaking up with?

7. What song does Phoebe join Chandler in mournfully singing while he's holding his ex's shoe after a break up?

8. What's the name of the dog that Phoebe sneaks into Monica and Chandler's apartment without Chandler knowing?

9. What movie comes on the new TV in Chandler's apartment that sucks Phoebe in to his and Joey's recliner club?

10. Chandler once hired Phoebe to temp in his office while his secretary was out for a few weeks, but he warned her that it might not be her thing because the job involved a lot of what?

Quotables:
Phoebe: Don't feel bad. You know they used to like you, a lot. But then you got promoted, and, you know, now you're all like "Mr. Boss Man." You know, Mr. Bing. Mr. Bing. "Boss Man Bing."
Chandler: I can't believe it.
Phoebe: Yeah, yeah. They even do you.
Chandler: They *do* me?
Phoebe: You know like... um, OK... um... *What comes next?*

Answers on page 155.

Season 10: Hard

Emma cries, a stripper cries, we all cry at the thought of our favorite show ending. Dry your tears and tackle these tough ones.

1. Where does Chandler keep his emergency pack of cigarettes?

2. According to what Phoebe tells Joey, what does a promise between friends mean?

3. When Joey reveals his plan to go with Monica and Chandler to their new house just to point out everything that's wrong with it and make them stay in the city, what does Mike call him?

4. When Phoebe, Ross and Rachel go clothes shopping, what's bedazzled on the back of the leather jacket that Phoebe suggests Ross try on?

5. For what product did Joey do a Japanese commercial, which is part of his audition tape for an advertising campaign of Chandler's?

6. What's the name of the stripper at Phoebe's bachelorette party?

7. What actress would Rachel like to play her if they ever made a movie about her life?

8. What book of Emma's does Joey do a dramatic reading of, moving everyone at her first birthday to tears?

9. When the guys are starving and locked out because they were late to Thanksgiving, they get excited when they remember that Monica put something in Joey and Rachel's oven. What was it?

10. What fake dinosaur name does Benjamin Hobart ask Ross to spell during his grant interview?

Quotables:
Janice: Ooh, that decides it then. I was on the fence. But knowing that you two would be our neighbors? Ah! Now we have to get it! Ellen, we're going to talk numbers. [Janice leaves with her realtor.]
Chandler: This cannot be happening!
Monica: OK, the realtor said another couple made an offer. Maybe the "Janices" won't get it! Maybe the other couple will.
Chandler: The only way that that is going to happen is...
What comes next?

Answers on page 156.

The One with All the Guest Stars

This category could truly go on for pages and pages, with the number of celebrities who stopped by "Friends" for an episode or three. Though only two of them, Christina Applegate and Bruce Willis, won Emmys for their guest acting efforts.

1. What "That Thing You Do!" actor plays Phoebe's ice dancer husband, Duncan?

2. Which A-Lister plays a woman who enacts a revenge plot, convincing Chandler to strip in a public bathroom and then stealing his clothes?

3. What Tony Award-winning actor plays Rachel's father, Leonard Green, in four episodes throughout the show?

4. What "Kids in the Hall" alum guest starred as Guru Saj, the herbalist Ross sees about his growth?

5. Who plays theater director Leonard Hayes, the man who prompts Joey for more intensity during an audition with inscrutable direction?

6. What "Glee" actress plays the realtor who is showing the house next to Monica and Chandler's where they run into Janice?

7. Who plays Phoebe's "Submarine Guy" boyfriend who gets chicken pox with her?

8. What "Riverdale" actor made his first appearance as Ben Geller in "The One That Could Have Been"?

9. Before she scored a long-running gig on "Criminal Minds," this actress was cast in one of her very first roles as Joey's girlfriend, Kathy, who Chandler later dates.

10. What "Star Trek: The Next Generation" actor has a one-episode spot as the Gucci executive who Rachel blows an interview with because her boss, Mr. Zelner, is at the next table?

Quotables:
Parker: Is something wrong?
Phoebe: Wrong? Really? You know the word wrong? Everything isn't perfect? Everything isn't magical? Everything isn't aglow with the light of a million fairies? They were just brake lights, Parker!
Parker: ... *What comes next?*

Answers on page 156.

Season 1: Difficult

*"Friends" was almost called "Insomnia Café" or "Six of One."
If you possess that kind of arcane knowledge, you're in good
shape for 10 seasons' worth of very difficult quizzes.*

1. Joey finds out his father is having an affair with what pet
mortician?

2. What wedding present does Rachel admit turned her on
more than Barry did?

3. What's the name of Chandler's boss who promotes him to
processing supervisor?

4. During a conversation about the strangest places they've
had sex, what does Monica tell the group, including her
brother — yikes, is her weirdest place?

5. Instead of theirs, the girls get George Stephanopoulos'
mushroom, green pepper and onion pizza by mistake instead
of theirs. What kind did they actually order?

6. What's the beeper number that Ross gets to alert him of
when Carol goes into labor?

7. Who is the peeper across the way with a telescope who
spies on the friends but is so charming on the phone they
forgive her?

8. According to a picture Monica finds, at what coffeehouse did her and Ross' grandmother regularly hang out with her friends?

9. Inspired by Chandler's mom, Rachel takes a stab at writing a romance novel. What's it called?

10. The Animal Control officer who shows up when Marcel goes missing went to high school with Monica and Rachel. Name her.

Quotables:
Ross: I can't believe you two had sex in her dream.
Chandler: I'm sorry, it was a one-time thing. ... *What comes next?*

Answers on page 157.

Rachel and Joey

Rachel and Joey arguably grew the most as friends over the series, from meeting for the very first time in the pilot to becoming roommates to almost coupling up at the start of the final season. (I think it's safe to say we're all glad that plotline tapped out early.)

1. Joey took Rachel as his date to an awards ceremony when he was nominated for what daytime television accolade?

2. What book does Joey give Rachel for her birthday in Season 1?

3. What phrase does Rachel yell at Joey on the boat that makes her stop in her tracks and realize how harsh she's been?

4. What did Joey once borrow one of Rachel's bras for?

5. Rachel and Joey agree to read one of each other's favorite books but end up spoiling them for each other — which books do they read?

6. When Joey says, "There's always room for Jell-O" in a sexy voice, Rachel asks him how he could possibly make that phrase dirty. He tells her it works for anything — then gives her what creepy example?

7. What does Rachel offer Joey as advice for what to do if any customers are rude to him when he's waiting tables?

8. Rachel moves in with Joey and learns it's not as big a deal to spill at his place as it is at Monica's. What food does she spill on the floor with gusto before Joey tells her not to waste it and scoops it back up on to his own plate?

9. When he's trying to get over his crush on her, what's the only item on Joey's list of things he doesn't like about Rachel?

10. What's the name of the heroine in the erotic novel of Rachel's that Joey finds and teases her about?

Quotables:
Joey: All right, Rach, the big question is, does he like you? All right? Because if he doesn't like you, this is all a moo point.
Rachel: Huh. A moo point?
Joey: Yeah, it's like… *What comes next?*

Answers on page 157.

Season 2: Difficult

The second season is the only one that doesn't have a full-fledged Thanksgiving episode – Mockolate notwithstanding. The plotline of Monica trying to create recipes with the chocolate substitute was added for the episode that aired on Nov. 16, 1995 at NBC's insistence at having a Thanksgiving-themed Must-See TV lineup. The rest of us just cared about Ross choosing between Rachel and Julie.

1. What kind of car did Phoebe's father steal from her mom when he ran out on them?

2. What movie is Marcel in New York filming when the gang visits him on the set?

3. Richard has a daughter named Michelle. What is her mother's name?

4. What did Barry's parents tell people was the reason that Rachel ran out on their wedding?

5. Who is the elderly woman whose soul Phoebe believes takes up residence in her body when she dies on her massage table?

6. What instrument did Chandler play in high school band?

7. When Monica is trying to get rich in the stock market, which three stocks does she purchase based on their ticker symbols?

8. Name the Jack Russell terrier that Phoebe accidentally runs over while attempting to meet her birth father.

9. At the Hootie and the Blowfish concert, Monica runs into the band's lawyer, who she used to babysit, and he gets them backstage. What's his name?

10. Where does Joey learn the words "jaunty" and "cachet"?

Quotables:
Ross: I don't believe this. I miss — I miss the first time of everything. I missed, what, the first time he rolled over, the first time he crawled. What else did I miss? Has he spoken yet, is he driving… *What comes next?*

Answers on page 158.

Mad About Monica

Monica often lamented her single status early in the show. That all changed in London when she and Chandler hooked up. Thank goodness that guy thought she was Ross' mom!

1. Whose boxer shorts does Monica throw into the Valentine's Day boyfriend bonfire?

2. What high school boyfriend of Rachel's does Monica go on a date with in Season 4?

3. While she's trying to get over Richard, what three things of his does Monica find that turn her into a mess again?

4. What's the name of the high school senior that Monica has a brief dalliance with (not knowing he was underage until later, of course)?

5. Rachel tells Monica that she looks like she slept with a hangar in her mouth after her tryst with who?

6. Where does Pete take Monica for pizza on their first date?

7. Name the sexy Latin waiter who Monica has a fling with at the diner.

8. Why does Monica break up with Timothy?

9. When Monica and Richard are briefly hooking up after their breakup, what's their euphemism for it?

---

10. Where does Mischa the translator invite Monica for a drink, tempting her with his diplomatic coupons?

Quotables:
Richard: All right, what about my two?
Monica: Well, it just seems like a really small number.
Richard: Right, and...
Monica: And, well... Don't you have a lot of wild oats to sow? Or is that what you're doing with me? *... What comes next?*

Answers on page 158.

Season 3: Difficult

This was the last year that the final episode of the season "Friends" finale wasn't an hourlong two-parter. We guess strip "Happy Days Game" only takes 22 minutes.

1. What's the name of the club where Ross kisses the hot girl from the Xerox place on the dance floor, leading to their one-night stand?

2. How many hot saves does Vince, Phoebe's fireman boyfriend, tell Chandler and Joey he had made?

3. Joey has seven sisters. Name them.

4. Who was Janice's first husband, and what does he go by professionally?

5. Where do Monica and Rachel get the hat they use to cover the bump on Ben's head?

6. For what product did Joey appear in an "Amazing Discoveries" infomercial?

7. What three things do Monica and Rachel compare Ross' look to when he shows up wearing the white suit with red bow tie that he didn't wear for a year because Rachel hated it?

8. What's the name of the former assassin – ahem, house painter – who Pete hires to train him for UFC fights?

9. Which five celebrities are on Chandler's "freebie list"?

10. According to Rachel, Ross played what song on his butt cheeks when he was hypnotized in Atlantic City?

Quotables:
Gunther: [Takes a drag of Chandler's cigarette] Oh, dark mother. Once again, I... *What comes next?*

Answers on page 159.

Ross and Chandler

College roommates who eventually become brothers-in-law and will always be tied together by unfortunate '80s hair. This difficult quiz will make you want to quit the gym.

1. What does Ross threaten to do to Chandler if he ever hurts Monica — speaking not as Chandler's best man but as her older brother?

2. What's the full name of Ross and Chandler's college buddy who they call the Party Wizard?

3. Ross came up with what nickname for Chandler after his toe severing that stuck for a year?

4. What hotel amenity that Ross had never thought of before does Chandler point out that they can take as part of the cost of the room?

5. What embarrassing item does Ross say Chandler brought with him to college?

6. What does Chandler first write on Ross' college alumni page that sets off their online battle?

7. What response does Ross coach Chandler to give when the gym employee goads him with "Don't you want a washboard stomach and rock-hard pecs?"

8. Along with their classmate Missy Goldberg, what three celebrities did Chandler and Ross have a pact that neither would go out with them?

9. What was Ross and Chandler's college band called?

10. What are the names on the fake IDs that college freshmen Ross and Chandler are planning to use on Thanksgiving break?

Quotables:
Chandler: Well, maybe you're going about this the wrong way. You know, I mean think about it. Single white male, divorced three times, two illegitimate children. The personal ad writes itself.
Ross: That's funny... So, do you think you'll ever work again?
Chandler: What are you doing? ... *What comes next?*

Answers on page 159.

Season 4: Difficult

Tate Donovan, who plays Joshua, and Jennifer Aniston dated for two years in real life, though not because they met on "Friends." In fact, he says they were breaking up right when he started his arc on the show. Awkward.

1. How many Oreos can Joey stuff in his mouth at one time?

2. After inflicting some damage playing rugby, what does Ross say was the last time he made a grown man cry?

3. When his gambit for a pretend airplane ticket doesn't work, how much does Chandler pay for his flight to Yemen, just to avoid Janice?

4. "Friends" was always a little fast and loose with age/birthday continuity. But according to what she tells Gunther, what's Rachel's birthday?

5. What are the three "tricks" that Joey tells the stripper from Ross' bachelor party that he's trained the duck to do?

6. What dance move does Joey do that proves to Monica and Rachel he's enjoying his ballroom practice with Treeger?

7. Chandler and Kathy watch a TV special about what comedian together in the canoe?

8. What service did Ross provide his high school soccer team?

9. Rhonda explains to Joey that museum tour guides and scientists don't sit with each other in the lunchroom. She gives an example about a scientist, Peter, and her not ever talking to each other even though they went to what elementary school together?

10. What fictional breakfast cereal does Ross suggest he wants to go eat in a bid to leave the dirty girl's apartment?

Quotables:
Salesman: So, what do you say, Joey? You get the whole set of encyclopedias for $1,200. That works out to just 50 bucks a book!
Joey: $1,200? You think I have $1,200? I'm home in the middle of the day and I got patio furniture in my living room. I guess... *What comes next?*

Answers on page 160.

The One with All the Songs

This quiz will test you on soundtrack songs, source music and when the characters themselves sing. Spoiler: None of these 10 questions are about Phoebe's music.

1. What song plays over the montage of Monica and Phoebe taking care of the Coma Guy?

2. Ross attempts to get Rachel to forgive him after he makes the list about her by requesting what song from a local radio station?

3. What's on the soundtrack when Joey arrives at his Las Vegas film set (just as they're shutting it down)?

4. After protesting she didn't want to do karaoke, what song does Monica immediately name when Mike and Phoebe press her to try it?

5. After first turning on the educational lecture by mistake, Ross puts on what romantic song in the planetarium when he and Rachel first… you know?

6. What song does Ross try to learn to play on the bagpipes?

7. Ross gets Emma to laugh for the first time by singing what inappropriate song?

8. Monica and Chandler kiss after finding the dice under the craps table to the strains of what song on the soundtrack?

9. What song does Ross use as the basis for his new answering machine message when he's living at Joey and Chandler's?

10. As the camera pans across the empty apartment in the final episode, what instrumental track can be heard?

Quotables:
Phoebe: New York City has no power | And the milk is getting sour | But to me it is not scary... *What comes next?*

Answers on page 160.

Season 5: Difficult

Ross and Emily's marriage was supposed to last a lot longer than it did, but the actress who played her became pregnant and was unavailable to film much in Season 5.

1. What three dorky portmanteaus does Monica come up with for her and Chandler's anniversary trip to Vegas?

2. According to Ross' count when they're in the couch store, how many times did he and Rachel have sex while they were together?

3. What grocery item was Phoebe's grandma reaching for when she died?

4. After he gets Ugly Naked Guy's apartment, what's Ross' apartment number in his new building?

5. In Season 5, the friends all make New Year's resolutions: Can you name all six?

6. What four things are in the box that Joey stashed under Monica's bed in case they ever got stuck in there again like during Ross and Rachel's breakup?

7. What two movies of Sam Waterston's does Joey's non-English speaking grandmother mention during her visit?

8. When Chandler arrives at Monica's with Champagne for a secret rendezvous, he finds Joey, Ross and Rachel also there

and comes up with a cover story about celebrating his office finally getting what?

9. According to The One with All the Thanksgivings, what year did Joey put a turkey on his head?

10. What did Joey and Chandler use the broiling pan they borrowed from Monica for?

Quotables:
Ross: Well, when you're subletting an apartment from your wife's cousin and then you get a divorce, sometimes the cousin suddenly wants his apartment back.
Chandler: How can he do that? Didn't you sign a lease?
Ross: Who needs a lease when it's *family*!
Joey: Hey, you can stay with us! We'll take care of ya!
Chandler: Oh, yeah! Absolutely! Anything you need man! But you have to promise me you will let us know the second you are feeling better so … *What comes next?*

Answers on page 161.

Monica and Joey

Here's a quiz about the guy who loves food and the chef: a perfect friendship from the start, despite Joey stripping naked in front of her on the first day they met.

1. When Chandler discovers that Joey lent money to Monica, what does Joey say it was for, hiding the fact that Monica needed it for bills because Chandler's still on an unpaid internship?

2. What food item of Joey's gets higher praise than Monica's in the cooking class?

3. When she's planning to go to the sperm bank, Joey tells Monica he thought she'd always end up with a blond guy, with a name like what?

4. Monica and Joey conspire to break up Joey's ex-girlfriend and her new boyfriend, so they can "keep the pieces for themselves." Name that couple.

5. How many pounds is the turkey that Monica agrees to cook for Thanksgiving in Season 8 because Joey promises to eat all of it?

6. When Monica hires Joey as a waiter so that she can fire him to show dominance over her disgruntled restaurant staff, what fake name does Joey go by?

7. What home improvement project does Joey start for Monica in the middle of building the entertainment unit?

8. Instead of narrowing down the choices, what does Joey add to Monica's list of appetizer options for her wedding menu?

9. When Monica tells Joey he can borrow her Porsche, what two things does she remind him that it's not?

10. What drink does Monica offer Joey on the day he moves in with Chandler that he thinks is code for wanting sex?

Quotables:
Monica: Wow! Wow! And it's definitely all gone? There's nothing there to work with? What were you thinking?
Joey: I don't know! I really want this part! And they tell you no matter what you get asked during an audition, you say yes. Like if-if they want you to ride a horse, you tell 'em you can! And you just figure out how to do it later.
Monica: Joey! This is not like learning to ride a horse! This is like... *What comes next?*

Answers on page 161.

Season 6: Difficult

Actress Maggie Wheeler played Janice, who appeared in 19 episodes of the series and often popped up at the most surprising times with her trademark "Oh. My. Gawd." and unique laugh. Season 6 is the only one that doesn't feature an actual Janice plotline — just her voice on a mix-tape.

1. In Phoebe's book about a couple and the arguments they have (that's actually about Monica and Chandler), what are the names of the main characters?

2. What sorority was Rachel a member of in college?

3. What three types of guys does Ross say will be lower on the dating totem pole than him, as Three Divorces Guy?

4. Joey asks Phoebe to accompany him on the drive back to New York from Las Vegas for company, saying they can reconnect as friends. What does Phoebe call the trip?

5. While trying to prove that his toys aren't too dangerous for babies, Chandler swallows a sonic blaster gun from what action figure?

6. What's the name of the redheaded child actor who Joey shows his hernia to in order to make him cry on camera?

7. The ring Chandler buys for Monica is a 1920s-style band with sapphires and what cut of diamond?

8. What real New York movie theater does Rachel say she and Ross are headed to when Phoebe pushes her into a cab so she can talk to Ross privately about the annulment?

9. When Ross walks in to find Chandler wearing rubber gloves and cleaning the apartment, he says couples who live together do start to look alike and gives him what new nickname?

10. According to Monica, what is Chandler's No. 3 favorite meal, which she cooks when she feels guilty about forgetting his Valentine's Day present?

Quotables:
Phoebe: Ross, you can't tell her not to go. You just started dating.
Ross: Then what am I supposed to do?
Phoebe: Nothing; you just have to be cool with it.
Ross: Well, what if she goes down and-and sleeps with a bunch of guys?
Chandler: Well, maybe... *What comes next?*

Answers on page 162.

Chandler's Girlfriends

Poor, lovelorn Chandler: funny, sweet and terrifyingly afraid of commitment. Until he finds his perfect match right across the hall, that is. Here's a quiz about Chandler pre-Monica.

1. Chandler and Kathy bond over their shared love of what infomercial product?

2. Why did Chandler dump his summer camp girlfriend, Julie Graff?

3. Who is the exotic woman Chandler dates who already has a husband and a boyfriend?

4. Chandler claims he broke up with Maureen Rasillo for what "real" reason?

5. How does Chandler describe Joanna, Rachel's boss, the first time he goes out with her?

6. What's printed on the candy hearts that Janice gives to Chandler after they hook up on Valentine's Day?

7. What co-star of Kathy's does Chandler worry she's having an affair with?

8. Why does Ginger, the girl with the prosthetic leg, break up with Chandler?

9. What woman does Chandler go out with after she mistakenly calls his number and he pretends to be her ex-boyfriend, Bob, on the phone?

10. With what woman does Chandler claim he had one of the greatest first dates in history, so good schoolchildren in the future will study it?

Quotables:
Janice: You probably want us to move in together?
Chandler: It doesn't scare me.
Janice: Yeah, well, it scares me! I mean I'm not even divorced yet, Chandler. You know, you just invited me over here for pasta, and all of the sudden you're, like, talking about moving in together. And I wasn't even that hungry. You know what? It's getting a little late, and I-I should just, um…
Chandler: Oh, no, no, no. Don't go! I've scared you! I've said too much! I'm… *What comes next?*

Answers on page 162.

Season 7: Difficult

It was during this season that NBC started the gimmick of "Super-sized" episodes of "Friends." Some episodes in Season 7 had a longer run time in a bid to compete with the hourlong ratings behemoth "Survivor" over on CBS.

1. What food item does Joey hold while practicing his award acceptance speech?

2. What's the name of the fictional comet that Ross has the whole gang on the roof to try to see?

3. How old was Monica when she learned to tell time?

4. Why did Rachel's dad buy her a boat when she was 15?

5. What's the name of the student who tries to get out of having failed his midterm by telling Ross he's in love with him?

6. Chandler kicks Joey out when he's trying to help him write his wedding vows because he makes what inappropriate suggestion?

7. What company does Phoebe work for when she's telemarketing?

8. What ill-fated online business did Jack lose a bunch of money on, meaning that the Gellers can't pay for Monica's wedding?

9. When Monica is trying to recreate Phoebe's grandmas cookies, which experimental batch made Ross hurl?

10. What heavy metal band does the competitive bride Monica meets at the dress store say her fiancée wants for their wedding?

Quotables:
Phoebe: I'm sorry, but I just wrote the best dance song for your wedding. Check this out.
Monica: No, Phoebe, I'll tell you what [grabs her guitar] — if you get ready now, I'll let you play it at the wedding.
Phoebe: Really?! Oh, that's so exciting! Thank you! Thanks, Mon! Oh, but Mon, if you touch my guitar again... *What comes next?*

Answers on page 163.

Rachel and Phoebe

The uptight, spoiled runaway bride and the hippie with a checkered past turned out to be great partners in crime, especially while they were roommates. We present a quiz about Rach and Pheebs.

1. When Phoebe pretends to be an actual Swedish massage therapist to fool Rachel, what name does she give her?

2. What perk convinces Phoebe to go the charity event for underprivileged kids with Rachel?

3. When Phoebe gets engaged to Mike, what gift does she give Rachel?

4. What two books is Rachel supposed to read for the literature class she takes with Phoebe but she doesn't?

5. What does Phoebe give Rachel as a going-away present when Rachel is headed for Paris?

6. What does Rachel call Phoebe's tactic of giving her a false negative on the pregnancy test to reveal how Rachel really felt about having a baby?

7. What four forms of ice does Phoebe provide for Rachel's surprise birthday party?

8. Rachel and Phoebe compete over who has claim to a "digital fairytale" after they find what at the coffeehouse?

9. What does Phoebe confess to Rachel while she's in labor with the triplets?

10. Why don't Rachel and Phoebe go back to living together after their apartment is renovated post-fire?

Quotables:
Phoebe: Really? So, this is... this is my big send-off into married life? Rachel, this is the only bachelorette party I'm ever gonna have! I've got a big wad of ones in my purse! Really? I mean, really? It's just tea?
Rachel: Nooo! Phoebe, of course there is more! I mean, I'll just go and talk to Monica and... *What comes next?*

Answers on page 163.

Season 8: Difficult

Season 8 premiered on Sept. 27, 2001, the first episode to air after the 9/11 attacks. The show, famously set in New York, honored the city's first responders throughout the year with visual references, including several characters wearing FDNY T-shirts.

1. What is Rachel's obstetrician's name?

2. What is the title of the World War I movie that Joey was filming during Monica and Chandler's wedding, which has its premiere during in Season 8?

3. Who is the Broadway producer who attends Monica and Chandler's wedding as Mrs. Bing's date and is subjected to Joey's dramatic overtures while he tries to score an audition?

4. At Thanksgiving, how much weight does Ross' old high school buddy Will say he's lost?

5. When Rachel is writing checks for trick or treaters, what little girl's name prompts her to write the check out to cash?

6. What two presents does Joey get for Jack and Judy on their 35th anniversary?

7. When Joey thinks Phoebe is pregnant, what name does she give him as the father who wants nothing to do with her or the baby (who is really just a kind of annoying guy from her gym)?

8. How many hours has Rachel been in labor when she finally goes to the delivery room?

9. What does Ross order at Central Perk after Mona dumps him?

10. While telling her father about her pregnancy, Rachel tells him that she is getting married, even though she's not. What two events does Phoebe say will make her too busy to go to the imaginary wedding?

Quotables:

Joey: Remember what happened the last time I did an interview for them? I said I write a lot of my own lines, and then the writers got mad and made my character fall down the elevator shaft. So, who knows what I might say this time?
Chandler: If only... *What comes next?*

Answers on page 164.

The One with All the Pop Culture

Try these questions about the movies, TV shows and celebrities that "Friends" namechecked over the course of its run. (In an ironic twist, now "Friends" is the cultural reference.)

1. What movie does Chandler recognize that Charlie is watching as he eavesdrops through her hotel room wall?

2. After Ross and Julie have sex – twice – Ross dances down the street to what classic musical number?

3. When Phoebe is covering for Rachel being pregnant, who does she say is the father of her child?

4. Chandler has two copies of the soundtrack of what musical?

5. Joey lands a part on this crime procedural, but he discovers when it airs that his scene was cut.

6. What TV character does Rachel mention in Phoebe's delivery room, upsetting the Fonzie-obsessed Dr. Harad?

7. Monica had a role in what play during high school?

8. What rare book does Chandler get for Kathy for her birthday, though he ends up having Joey give it to her?

9. Which movie are Rachel and Joey watching when he realizes that he has feelings for her?

10. When Ross suggests he and Chandler go to the Hard Rock Café for dinner again because he really likes the food, what does Chandler assert is the real reason he wants to go there?

Quotables:
Monica: Wait a minute... Ross and Charlie, Joey and Rachel, Phoebe and Mike! We're the only people leaving with the same person we came with.
Chandler: That's not true. I came with Monica and... *What comes next?*

Answers on page 164.

Season 9: Difficult

After an intense salary renegotiation that could have ended the show, NBC gave the cast their asking price of an astonishing $1,000,000 per episode — each — starting in Season 9.

1. What three restaurants does Chandler mention when he talks to Monica about finding a job in the dining hotbed that is Tulsa, Oklahoma?

2. Joey finally gets a romantic storyline on "Days of Our Lives." What's the name of the woman his character is romancing?

3. What are Mike's Upper East Side parents' names?

4. When Chandler's company moves him to Tulsa, he doesn't get a raise, but they do offer him what perk?

5. What's Rachel's grandmother's name?

6. What's the name of the beautiful woman from college who shows up at Ross' memorial, only to be terrified when he comes out of the guest bedroom to reveal he's not dead?

7. What does Chandler futilely use to try to cover up the smell of cigarette smoke on his clothes when he gets back from Tulsa?

8. Outside what business did young Phoebe rob young Ross?

9. What was the subject line of the email that Chandler opened on Ross' computer that gave it a virus and erased his paleontology conference keynote speech?

10. To make him feel better when Ross and Rachel question his responsibility to parent, what does Monica tell Chandler that Emma is the product of?

Quotables:
Ross: I know! I mean a PhD is just as good as an MD.
Rachel: Yeah, oh sure, Ross, yeah! If I have a heart attack at a restaurant... *What comes next?*

Answers on page 165.

Ross and Joey

Book smarts, meet street smarts: Ross and Joey had a lot to offer each other. In later years, Ross even refers to Chandler as his oldest friend and Joey as his best friend. Aww.

1. What two toiletries does Joey suggest that Ross use in an effort to get his heat-shrunk leather pants back on?

2. Joey tells Ross to punch him to get even for his accidental proposal to Rachel, but he ducks and Ross breaks his thumb by punching what?

3. Why do Ross and Joey get stuck on the roof after watching for the comet?

4. When Joey works as a tour guide at Ross' museum, Joey learns that what two distinct groups of people never sit together at lunch?

5. While Ross is super bored on sabbatical and looking for a project, he volunteers to help keep Joey on track doing what?

6. What do Ross and Joey do with the extra seat they have because Chandler doesn't go to the Rangers game on thanksgiving?

7. Which of Joey's solo apartment décor items does Ross buy for him to save it from being repossessed?

8. Joey once thought Ross' name was short for something. What two names did he think might be the long version?

9. Joey appears to dive to cover Ross during the ride-along, angering Chandler, but it turns out he was instinctively protecting what?

10. What's the name of the new girl in the neighborhood who Joey and Ross are dating at the same time, leading to an awkward secret-spilling dinner?

Quotables:
Joey: Six months? Whoa, that's rough.
Ross: Well, I mean it's not all bad. I'm learning to appreciate the uh, smaller things in life. Like the sound of a bird and the color of the sky.
Joey: ... *What comes next?*

Answers on page 165.

Season 10: Difficult

The finale of "Friends" aired on May 6, 2004, garnering 52.46 million viewers. That didn't make it the most-watched of the series, however. That title belongs to the two-part "The One After the Super Bowl" from way back in Season 2, which pulled in 52.9 million thanks to a slew of guest stars and its NFL lead-in.

1. What's Joey's Cabbage Patch Kid named?

2. What kinky thing does Chandler say he once did for Monica?

3. Aside from Benjamin Hobart, what two people does Ross mention would be at his fantasy dinner party?

4. What's the full name of Monica and Phoebe's old friend who has been living in England and has picked up an annoying fake accent?

5. Name the guy who eats paper, Estelle's only other client besides Joey.

6. How does Chandler describe his little black book?

7. What two things does Joey ask for when Monica and Chandler tell him that he has his own room in their house?

8. While staying at Rachel's father's house, Ross discovers that his refrigerator contains nothing but what two items?

9. Phoebe tells Mike that women appreciate what two things?

10. In what order does Rachel say goodbye to everyone (except Ross) at her going-away party?

Quotables:
Joey: You know, I had a chance to stop her, too.
Ross: Yeah?
Joey: Who loses 57 coin tosses in a row? Heads, she wins; tails, I lose. [Joey stops, realizing something] Wait a minute...
Chandler: Yes, Joe?
Joey: ... *What comes next?*

Answers on page 166.

Phoebe's Flings

Phoebe really knew how to play the field; she may have had more short-term relationships than Joey. Try your hand at this quiz about her loves up to and including her husband, Mike.

1. Phoebe meets a guy named Larry at Monica's restaurant and they date for a minute — what's his job?

2. Phoebe cringingly tells Mike's mom that he is a very gentle lover, but that he can also do what?

3. What's the name of Phoebe's athletic boyfriend who is always "coming out of his shorts"?

4. Phoebe starts dating someone the girls nicknamed Cute Coffeehouse Guy. What nickname do the guys have for him?

5. Who is the psychiatrist who Phoebe dates who analyzes everyone in the group, making them hate him?

6. Thinking she's her twin sister, what stalker starts following Phoebe?

7. Phoebe says the fur coat is the best thing she's ever had wrapped around her — including what "fine" ex-boyfriend?

8. Thinking he was Ralph Lauren, who did Phoebe make out with at Rachel's office?

9. Why does Phoebe break up with Tim, Monica's sous chef?

10. In what neighborhood were Phoebe and Gary looking for apartments to move into together?

Quotables:
Chandler: So, you must be going to somewhere fancy to celebrate?
Phoebe: Uh-uh. Um, a Knicks game.
Joey: Um... Aren't you a little overdressed?
Phoebe: Hey, you know what, I've never had a one-year anniversary before, so no matter where we go, I'm wearing something fancy pants, and I'm gonna put on my finest jewelry and... *What comes next?*

Answers on page 166.

Expert Quiz 1

Are you ready for the ultimate trivia challenge? This and the next two quizzes require a "Friends" PhD. Questions can come from any season or facts about the show itself. Good luck!

1. According to Rachel's invitation to Ross and Emily's wedding, what's the address of Monica's apartment?

2. Name the actress who plays Chloe.

3. Rachel asks Phoebe and Monica and Chandler to find her a date for a charity event, and a competition ensues as they try to get her to pick the guys they selected. What are the names of those two guys?

4. What is Joey's ATM pin?

5. How many times did Fat Monica appear on the show?

6. What three home décor stores does Ross mention when he and Joey are discussing the latter's enormous Visa bill?

7. What was Rachel's flight number to Paris?

8. Before Rachel accidentally dumps a box of photos all over Monica's neat stack of pictures, Monica shows her the prototype for the new organizational system she's numbering the photos with — what number is the prototype?

9. When Joey and Chandler are heading to Vegas, Ross asks them to place a $20 bet on what roulette number?

10. What's Monica and Chandler's wedding date, including the year?

Quotables:
Frank Jr.: My mother didn't want us to be together, but the worst she ever did was tie me to the porch!
Phoebe: Well…
Frank Jr.: Wait, y'know what, I came to you because I thought you'd understand! Oh, no! Y'know, I would storm out of here right now if… *What comes next?*

Answers on page 167.

Expert Quiz 2

1. Friends aired six clip shows during its 10-season run. The One with the Invitation was the first, in Season 4. Can you name the other five?

2. Who took the SATs for Rachel in high school?

3. What does Chandler facetiously tell Phoebe cigarettes are called in Hawaii?

4. While faking the "Ross makes a toast" photo at a stranger's wedding to replace Monica's lost disposable cameras, Ross, prompted by the guests to make an actual toast, instead makes an announcement about what kind of car being towed?

5. Joey finds a check stub from what ring designer in Pete's checkbook, prompting the gang to think he's proposing to Monica?

6. What neighbor lives underneath Joey and Chandler's apartment?

7. What is Phoebe's address, including apartment number?

8. How many boxes of Brown Bird cookies did Ross sell?

9. David Schwimmer plays Ross' doppelganger, Russ, but he's listed in the credits as what?

10. On what date did the pilot episode of "Friends" premiere?

Quotables:
Treeger: You're clogging up the chute I just spent 30 minutes unclogging!
Rachel: I'm sorry. I don't come in here a lot.
Treeger: Oh, yeah, of course you don't. 'Cause you're a little princess. Daddy, buy me a pizza. Daddy, buy me a candy factory. Daddy,... *What comes next?*

Answers on page 167.

134

Expert Quiz 3

1. What Warner Bros. backlot stage was renamed the Friends Stage after the final season wrapped, because the show shot there from Season 2-10?

2. What is Janice's maiden name?

3. At his birthday party, Jack is looking for his baseball bat signed by what player?

4. What are the names of the two imaginary kids Joey creates for his character, Joseph the processor, when he's working with Chandler?

5. What are the names of Chandler's Tulsa secretary's three cats?

6. What's Rachel's room number in Barbados?

7. Who is the actor who portrayed Ugly Naked Guy?

8. What three people had died while Phoebe was at the dentist, convincing her she was cursed?

9. What size shoes does Joey wear?

10. What are Chandler's three tricks to why he's so good at tweezing eyebrows?

Quotables:

Janice: By the way, Chandler. I cut you out of all my pictures. So if you want, I have a bag with just your heads.
Chandler: That's OK.
Janice: Oh, are you sure? Really? Because you know, you could make little puppets out of them, and you could... *What comes next?*

Answers on page 168.

Answers

Season 1: Easy
1. Mr. Heckles
2. A lasagna
3. Ursula
4. Überweiss
5. Al Pacino
6. Kung Pao Chicken
7. Monana
8. M, O, and K
9. Underdog
10. Freud!

Quotables answer: I'll use the gentle cycle.
— *The One with the East German Laundry Detergent*

Ross and Rachel
1. Ross
2. "Frankie Say Relax"
3. The planetarium
4. Spoiled, ditzy, too into her looks, just a waitress, chubby ankles
5. At the laundromat
6. Rachel kissed Gavin
7. 18 pages, front and back
8. Bonus Night
9. Ross
10. Pizza Hut

Quotables answer: Woken up feeling comforted and satisfied!

— The One Where Joey Speaks French

Season 2: Easy

1. The One with the Prom Video
2. Smell-the-fart acting
3. Gunther
4. "Smelly Cat"
5. Dr. Drake Ramoray
6. Our Little Harmonica
7. He grows a mustache
8. Deviated septum
9. Turned it into a gym
10. Eddie Menuek

Quotables Answer: It's Isaac Newton, and he's pissed.
— The One Where Heckles Dies

The One with All the Animals
1. Paolo
2. Fluffy Meowington
3. Chuck and Dick
4. Mrs. Whiskerson
5. Mitsy
6. Chi-Chi
7. Julio
8. Her mom's dog kept looking at him
9. Chappy
10. Rats

Quotables Answer: They're ugly and stupid and delicious!
— The One with the Rumor

Season 3: Easy
1. Mary Angela
2. Drink a glass of fat
3. A racecar bed
4. Chloe, the hot girl from the Xerox place
5. Magna-Doodle
6. Montauk
7. Chopsticks
8. Joey and Janice's Day of Fun
9. A troll doll nailed to a 2-by-4
10. He puts it in the freezer

Quotables Answer: If it's not a headboard, it's just not worth it.
— *The One with the Giant Poking Device*

Joey and Chandler
1. A canoe
2. Rolos
3. "To my best bud."
4. Fireball
5. He's dead inside
6. A bag of plastic spoons
7. Pat, the ceramic dog
8. He falls asleep
9. Cups
10. Six hours

Quotables Answer: Stop the Q-Tip when there's resistance!
— *The One with Ross' New Girlfriend*

Season 4: Easy

1. Monica
2. V
3. 11
4. Chandler and Monica hooked up
5. Leslie, Frank Jr. Jr. and Chandler
6. How you doin'?
7. A waiter spilled water down her back, she jumped up and her boob popped out
8. Yemen
9. It's not that common, it doesn't happen to every guy and it is a big deal!
10. Joanna

Quotables Answer: Office Max!
— *The One with the Dirty Girl*

Romancing Rachel

1. Paolo
2. Spin the Bottle
3. Tag Jones
4. Dr. Franzblau
5. Danny
6. Billy Dreskin
7. Kash Ford
8. Chicken boy
9. Michael
10. Tommy

Quotables Answer: I got the date. I'm just not on it.
— *The One with Rachel's Crush*

Season 5: Easy
1. Huggsy
2. Cups and ice
3. Pivot
4. He's a dropper
5. A mustache and beard
6. Phoebe and Gary
7. That he not see Rachel ever again
8. Ugly Naked Guy's apartment
9. Air purifier
10. A fez and yellow oversize sunglasses

Quotables Answer: Just the one divorce in '99!
— *The One with All the Resolutions*

Monica and Phoebe
1. Jason Hurley
2. Waxine
3. Javu
4. Phoebe's grandmother's chocolate chip cookie recipe
5. Catering
6. Dudley Moore
7. Catwoman and Supergirl
8. A giant dog, a ghost, and a dinosaur
9. Monica makes sex noises during them
10. She picks Phoebe up and shakes it out of her pants

Quotables Answer: It'll be like I have a wife in the '50s!
— *The One with the Dirty Girl*

Season 6: Easy
1. Pottery Barn

2. Unagi
3. A Porsche
4. Denise
5. Phoebe's
6. A yacht
7. NYU
8. The Barcalounger
9. English Trifle and Shepherd's Pie
10. Ross

Quotables:
Answer: The guy stopped drawing the deer.
— *The One Where Chandler Can't Cry*

The One with All the Siblings
1. Seven
2. She bought a boat
3. Take one of his kids
4. Gets Emma's ears pierced
5. Dairy
6. Bobby Corso
7. Sold it to a Swedish runaway
8. The hottest girl I've ever hated
9. Ninja stars
10. A tattoo on her ankle

Quotables Answer: I counted them when they were coming out of my area.
— *The One Where Ross Is Fine*

Season 7: Easy
1. Monica was actually looking for a fling with Joey that night

2. Rosita
3. The Holiday Armadillo
4. That she is actually 31
5. Ross and Joey
6. Chandler
7. Ray-ray
8. Bagpipes
9. Their beach house
10. Ross and Joey

Quotables Answer: You may not get invited.
— *The One with Rachel's Book*

Ross and Monica

1. The Routine
2. Saying "Check!" to themselves when they pack something
3. 1250
4. Geller Bowl VI
5. Dr. Gettleman
6. "Predators of the Serengeti"
7. The Moistmaker
8. The Geller Yeller
9. Ross stole his dad's Playboys, Monica broke the porch swing, Ross got fired from the museum, Monica and Chandler are living together, Ross married Rachel in Vegas and Ross got divorced – AGAIN
10. Ross bought a sports car and Monica got drunk

Quotables Answer: I love that man. He's like a brother to — Dad.
— *The One Where Ross and Rachel... You Know*

Season 8: Easy
1. Muriel
2. Red sweater
3. A key to his apartment
4. Janice
5. A toy boat
6. Bamboozled
7. Boots
8. Her mom
9. His grandmother's engagement ring
10. Ken Adams

Quotables Answer: Can I interest you in a sarcastic comment?
— *The One with the Tea Leaves*

The One with All the Travel
1. Barbados
2. "London, baby!"
3. Vail
4. Atlantic City
5. Connecticut
6. Greece
7. One-year anniversary
8. Minsk
9. Aruba
10. Massapequa

Quotables Answer: I give you these candies?
— *The One in Vegas, Part 1*

Season 9: Easy
1. Joey

2. Chandler
3. Emma Geller-Green
4. He doesn't
5. Wendy
6. Charlie Wheeler
7. Sandy
8. Ping pong
9. Phoebe
10. Her shirt is see-through in the spotlight

Quotables Answer: Those nerds would get laaaaaid!
— The One with the Fertility Test

Rachel and Chandler
1. Mama's Little Bakery, Chicago, Illinois
2. Her Walkman
3. Travel Scrabble
4. Patrick
5. "Happy Birthday, Grandma. It's better to be over the hill than buried under it!"
6. The Fear
7. Her passport
8. Wetting the bed
9. "Time of the Season" by the Zombies
10. "Melrose Place"

Quotables Answer: Whatever, Linus, I'm opening mine.
— The One with the Routine

Season 10: Easy
1. French
2. Estelle

3. Swings
4. "Pyramid"
5. Princess Consuela Banana-Hammock
6. They entered Emma in a beauty pageant
7. Jack and Erica
8. "I got off the plane."
9. Chandler says "Where?"
10. Monica's yellow peephole picture frame

Quotables Answer: What did I marry into?
— *The One Where the Stripper Cries*

Ross' Relationships
1. Vermont
2. Saltwater taffy
3. It's a Small World
4. Caitlin
5. Graduate school
6. Poughkeepsie
7. Celia
8. Elizabeth Hornswoggle
9. Cutie McPretty
10. She gets back together with her ex

Quotables Answer: Look like they should live under a bridge!
— *The One with the Home Study*

Season 1: Hard
1. "There's nothing to tell."
2. Scranton
3. Lorraine
4. Her Aunt Sylvia

5. Lizzy
6. Tiki Death Punch
7. Mario
8. Grilled cheese fixin's, tomato soup and a family size bag of Funyuns
9. The Russian Tea Room
10. Weekly Estimated Net Usage Statistics (or Systems, Chandler says the acronym both ways in Season 1)

Quotables Answer: You have to put 'em together yourself, but they cost a little less.
— *The One with All the Poker*

Joey and Phoebe
1. Bear Claw, Turkey Leg, Old Lady, Tiger, Dragon, Iceberg
2. He's brand new
3. A selfless good deed
4. Annie
5. Discuss the rest of the group
6. "Excellent butt, great rack."
7. A bologna sandwich and a pickle
8. "You don't expect someone so hot to be so sweet."
9. Nurse with tray
10. When she breaks up with him as Ursula, when she gives him feedback on his kissing for an audition, on her 30th birthday when she realizes she's actually 31, when he proposes to her thinking she's pregnant and when Joey is starving and she finally says "let's just order" at her birthday dinner

Quotables Answer: There's no meat in beer, right?
— *The One with the Fake Party*

Season 2: Hard

1. Monkeyshine Beer
2. Hermit Junction
3. He has a "Twinkie in the city"
4. The Little General
5. Roy Gublik
6. Bryce, died in an avalanche
7. Todd
8. "Be Your Own Windkeeper"
9. My Big Book of Grievances
10. Lobster, peanuts and kiwi

Quotables Answer: Which sister?
— *The One Where Joey Moves Out*

The One with All the Weddings

1. Lavender
2. Slippery shoes
3. Frannie
4. Greek Orthodox
5. Ross
6. Steel drums
7. "Copacabana" by Barry Manilow
8. Melinda, Ashley and Gert
9. The church Emily wants to use as a venue is being torn down
10. 128

Quotables Answer: Well, I guess we can all agree that's not gonna happen!
— *The One with Barry and Mindy's Wedding*

Season 3: Hard

1. Sergio Valente
2. Leslie
3. Ross, Chandler and Rachel versus Joey, Monica and Phoebe
4. "Boxing Day"
5. Power, precision and panache
6. Moss 865
7. Peep-eye
8. Hummus
9. Dr. Robert Bobby
10. Winona Ryder

Quotables Answer: No, only for sex.
— *The One Where Chandler Can't Remember Which Sister*

Rachel and Monica

1. Because she loses her stuff
2. Tommy Rollerson
3. She sees Rachel spit out Champagne at her wedding reception
4. Jean-Claude Van Damme
5. Seashell lamp
6. Little round waffle iron
7. She lets you borrow her boots, gets catalogs and folds down pages of things you might like, leaves notes on the shower mirror, covers you with a blanket when you fall asleep on the couch
8. Wendy
9. A frisee salad with goat cheese and pine nuts, wild rice, roasted asparagus and salmon en croute

10. They kiss each other for one minute

Quotables Answer: They told us that was for the mascot!
— *The One with the Cat*

Season 4: Hard
1. Leather pants, regular coffee and tequila
2. Picturing yourself with other women
3. Wordless sound poems
4. It gives him time to think about what he did, it proves how much he cares about Joey and it hurts
5. Helen Baxendale
6. She can only eat them in even numbers
7. A movie stub from their first date, an eggshell from when he cooked her breakfast in bed and a fossil from the museum where they first… you know
8. Fears and Pet Peeves, Ancient History, Literature and It's All Relative
9. A Toblerone
10. She rented it from a store called It's Not Too Late

Quotables Answer: Order the channel that carries the sport.
— *The One with All the Rugby*

The One with All the Porn
1. Treeger
2. "Buffay the Vampire Layer," "Lawrence of A Labia," "Inspect Her Gadget," "Sex Toy Story 2"
3. "You know, that's bad for the paper tray."
4. Shark porn
5. "Dr. Do-Me-A-Little"
6. "Good Will Humping"

7. A basket of porn
8. Busty Ladies
9. Playboy
10. "Candy and Cookie"

Quotables Answer: You got porn!
— *The One with Rachel's Book*

Season 5: Hard
1.There was never any parking by the psychology building
2. Bendy
3. Beautiful fall weather and thongs
4. Angus
5. A lost eyelash curler and seeing Donald Trump waiting for an elevator
6. 1 penny for every dollar the movie makes
7. "Emotional Knapsack"
8. Happy and sick
9. Nutter Butter
10. "Kids welcome here" and "Come here to me"

Quotables Answer: Not nature, fashion!
— *The One with the Yeti*

Ross and Phoebe
1. Ross can!
2. Whitney and Kyle
3. Gives massages to her clients
4. A bike
5. He called her boring
6. Salt, bread and a scented candle
7. Lowell

8. He has words with Phoebe and she kills him
9. Renyard's theory of species variegation
10. He didn't chip in for the handyman, he raised his own hand as an answer to "Who here likes Ross" and he's wearing two nametags

Quotables Answer: Who put those fossils there, and why?
— *The One Where Heckles Dies*

Season 6: Hard
1. Phoebe Buffay, Buried Alive
2. Female roommate, non-smoker, non-ugly
3. He went to Egypt with his dad
4. An old shoe in a Macy's bag
5. Couples spa day and crotchless panties
6. A police horse
7. She rubs Vapo-Rub on her chest
8. The Mr. Beaumont
9. His slide projector
10. Scotch on the rocks with a twist on a coaster

Quotables Answer: I've never had to use the other one.
— *The One with the Ring*

Joey Has a Date
1. Lauren
2. Soleil Moon Frye
3. LeCroix
4. Melanie
5. Felicity
6. Angela Delvecchio
7. Three chocolate mousses

8. Denise DiMarco
9. Annabel
10. Erika Ford

Quotables Answer: Closeness-shmoshness! There was three of us for crying out loud!
— *The One with the Cop*

Season 7: Hard

1. Stephanopoulos and Acidophilus
2. Hilda
3. Helena Handbasket
4. Jessica Lockhart
5. Hexadrin
6. La-Z-Boy E-cliner 3000
7. Diane Keaton
8. Space Mountain
9. The Bay City Rollers
10. He wants to leave before Joey gets worked up and starts calling everybody bitch

Quotables Answer: You have to respect the sea!
— *The One with Phoebe's Cookies*

Monica and Chandler

1. A high-speed chase
2. Tennis
3. Greg and Jenny
4. Chandler
5. He wrote her a rap song
6. Monica opened all the presents and Chandler kissed someone else faking the disposable camera pictures

7. A piece of carrot
8. A hard eight (Two fours)
9. "There's a reason why girls don't do this!"
10. A sock bunny and a mix-tape

Quotables Answer: Whose wife made him die inside.
— *The One with the Male Nanny*

Season 8: Hard
1. Twizzlers
2. Jamaican
3. Brenda
4. Faded salmon
5. Cliff
6. Isabella and Delilah
7. Mount Tibidabo
8. "Oh, crap!"
9. Sandra Green
10. Chandler's boss, Doug

Quotables Answer: I'll prove it like a theorem!
— *The One with the Halloween Party*

The One with All the Jobs
1. Fortunata Fashions
2. He wears roller blades
3. Caesar's Palace
4. Alessandro's
5. "Not suitable for adults"
6. She is caught making out with a client
7. Saks Fifth Avenue
8. Joey

9. Sediment flow rate

10. Duties

Quotables Answer: Your work makes me sad.

— *The One Where Everybody Finds Out*

Season 9: Hard

1. Mr. Wigglemunch and the Grumpus
2. Garlic
3. Gleba
4. The Land Where Time Stands Still
5. Stop-eating hot
6. "Got milk?"
7. Dr. Weiner
8. Monica was going to eat him
9. Veal
10. Hit by a blimp

Quotables Answer: You are so lazy. Can't you get on top for once?

— *The One with the Blind Dates*

Chandler and Phoebe

1. Fight all your natural instincts
2. $1
3. A Revolutionary War musket
4. Feel his bicep and more
5. Spider-Man
6. Janice and Tony
7. "Endless Love" by Lionel Richie
8. Clunkers
9. "Xanadu"

10. Being normal for a large portion of the day

Quotables Answer: "Could that report BE any later?"
— *The One with the Ick Factor*

Season 10: Hard
1. Taped to the back of the toilet tank
2. Never having to give a reason
3. A strange kind of grown-up
4. "Boys will be boys"
5. Ichiban lipstick for men
6. Roy Goodbody
7. Claire Danes
8. "Love You Forever"
9. Brussels sprouts
10. Mboscodictiasaur

Quotables Answer: If the other couple are the Hitlers!
— *The One Where Estelle Dies*

The One with All the Guest Stars
1. Steve Zahn
2. Julia Roberts
3. Ron Liebman
4. Kevin McDonald
5. Jeff Goldblum
6. Jane Lynch
7. Charlie Sheen
8. Cole Sprouse
9. Paget Brewster
10. Brent Spiner

Quotables Answer: Well, excuse me for putting a good spin on a traffic jam!
— *The One in Massapequa*

Season 1: Difficult
1. Ronni Rapalano
2. A Limoges gravy boat
3. Big Al Costilick
4. On top of a pool table, senior year of college
5. Fat-free crust with extra cheese
6. 55-JIMBO
7. Sidney Marks
8. Java Joe's
9. "A Woman Undone"
10. Luisa Gianetti

Quotables Answer: I was very drunk and it was someone else's subconscious.
— *The One with the Ick Factor*

Rachel and Joey
1. A Soapie
2. "Oh! The Place You'll Go" by Dr. Seuss
3. "Greens don't quit!"
4. To fling water balloons
5. "Little Women" and "The Shining"
6. Grandma's chicken salad
7. Sneeze muffin
8. Spaghetti
9. She made him switch to light mayonnaise
10. Zelda

Quotables Answer: A cow's opinion. It just doesn't matter. It's moo.
— *The One Where Chandler Doesn't Like Dogs*

Season 2: Difficult
1. Gremlin
2. "Outbreak 2: The Virus Takes Manhattan"
3. Barbara
4. She was insane from syphilis
5. Rose Adelman
6. Clarinet
7. MEG, ZXY, and CHP
8. Schnoodle
9. Stevie Fisher
10. Word of the Day toilet paper

Quotables Answer: Does he have a favorite liqueur?
— *The One Where Old Yeller Dies*

Mad About Monica
1. Adam Ritter
2. Chip Matthews
3. A cigar butt, a clump of drain hair, Civil War videos
4. Ethan
5. Paul the Wine Guy
6. Rome
7. Julio
8. His kiss reminds her of his father, Richard
9. Playing racquetball
10. The Rainbow Room

Quotables Answer: Oh, my God! Am I an oat?

— *The One Where Dr. Ramoray Dies*

Season 3: Difficult
1. The Philly
2. 98
3. Dina, Tina, Gina, Mary Angela, Mary Therese, Cookie and Veronica
4. Gary Litman, the Mattress King
5. Rainy Day Bear
6. The Milk-Master 2000
7. Colonel Sanders, Riverboat captain, inventor of the cotton gin
8. Hoshi
9. Kim Basinger, Cindy Crawford, Halle Berry, Yasmine Bleeth and Jessica Rabbit
10. "Wipe Out"

Quotables Answer: Suckle at your smoky teat.
— *The One with the Hypnosis Tape*

Ross and Chandler
1. Hunt him down and kick his ass
2. Mike "Gandalf" Ganderson
3. Sir Limps-A-Lot
4. Batteries from the remote control
5. Security blanket
6. Ross has sex with dinosaurs
7. "No! I want a flabby gut and saggy man-breasts!"
8. Phoebe Cates, Molly Ringwald and Sheena Easton
9. Way, No Way
10. Roland Chang and Clifford Alvarez

Quotables Answer: You know I can only dish it out!
— *The One Where Monica Sings*

Season 4: Difficult
1. 15
2. When he was 4 and washed his dad's Porsche with rocks
3. $2,100
4. May 5
5. Stare at the wall, hardly move, be white
6. A pas de bourrée
7. Ernie Kovacs
8. Organized their game schedules on his Commodore 64
9. P.S. 129
10. Cinnamon Fruit Toasties

Quotables Answer: There's a few things you don't get from book learnin'.
— *The One with the Cuffs*

The One with All the Songs
1. "My Guy" by Mary Wells
2. "With or Without You" by U2
3. "A Horse with No Name" by America
4. "Delta Dawn" by Tanya Tucker
5. "Wicked Game" by Chris Isaak
6. "Celebration" by Kool and the Gang
7. "Baby Got Back" by Sir Mix-A-Lot
8. "Everybody Loves Somebody" by Dean Martin
9. "We Will Rock You" by Queen
10. "Embryonic Journey" by Jefferson Airplane

Quotables Answer: 'Cause I stay away from dairy

— *The One with the Blackout*

Season 5: Difficult
1. Plane-aversary, anni-Vegas-ary and A-Nevada-versary
2. 298
3. Yogurt
4. 3B
5. Joey wants to learn guitar, Monica will take more pictures, Ross will do a new thing every day, Rachel will stop gossiping, Chandler will stop making fun of his friends and Phoebe will learn to pilot a commercial jet
6. Candy bars, crossword puzzles, MadLibs and condoms
7. "Crimes and Misdemeanors" and "Capricorn One"
8. Wrinkle-free fax paper
9. 1992
10. The duck was throwing up caterpillars

Quotables Answer: That we can make fun of your hair!
— *The One Where Ross Moves In*

Monica and Joey
1. A boob job
2. Cookies
3. Hoyt
4. Angela and Bob
5. 19 pounds
6. Dragon
7. Retiling the bathroom floor
8. Peanut butter fingers
9. A place to entertain his lady friends and a place to eat spaghetti
10. Lemonade

Quotables Answer: Learning to grow a turtleneck!
— *The One with Ross and Monica's Cousin*

Season 6: Difficult
1. Marcia and Chester
2. Kappa Kappa Delta
3. Four Divorces Guy, Murder Guy and Geologists
4. A friennaissance
5. Krog
6. Alex
7. Princess
8. The Angelika
9. Mondler
10. Macaroni and cheese with cut up hot dogs

Quotables Answer: You don't marry this one.
— *The One with Joey's Fridge*

Chandler's Girlfriends
1. A Wonder Broom
2. She got fat
3. Aurora
4. She didn't hate Yanni
5. A big, dull dud
6. Chan and Jan Forever
7. Nick
8. She discovers his nubbin
9. Jade
10. Danielle

Quotables Answer: Hopeless and awkward and desperate for love!
— *The One with the Metaphorical Tunnel*

Season 7: Difficult
1. Maple syrup
2. Bapstein-King
3. 13
4. To cheer her up because her pony was sick
5. Ned Morse
6. "Monica, I love your sweet ass"
7. Empire Office Supplies
8. Selling ice
9. Batch 16
10. Carcass

Quotables Answer: I'm going to have to pound on you a little bit.
— *The One with Monica's Thunder*

Rachel and Phoebe
1. Ikea
2. Open bar
3. Her little black book
4. "Jane Eyre" and "Wuthering Heights"
5. A cotton swab with her saliva on it so she can clone her own Pheebs
6. A risky little game
7. Crushed, cubed, dry and Sno-Cones
8. A cute guy's cell phone
9. She wants to keep one

10. The remodel turned it from a two-bedroom to a one-bedroom

Quotables Answer: Get an ETA on the pee-pees!
— *The One Where the Stripper Cries*

Season 8: Difficult
1. Dr. Long
2. "Over There"
3. Dennis Phillips
4. 150 pounds
5. Lelani Mayolanofavich
6. A star named after them and a book on Kama Sutra for the elderly
7. David Lynn
8. 21
9. Warm milk
10. Unicorn baptism and leprechaun bar mitzvah

Quotables Answer: There was something in your head to control the things you say.
— *The One with Joey's Interview*

The One with All the Pop Culture
1. "Miss Congeniality"
2. "Singin' in the Rain"
3. James Brolin
4. "Annie"
5. "Law and Order"
6. Mork
7. "The Sound of Music"
8. First-edition "Velveteen Rabbit"

9. "Cujo"
10. The "Purple Rain" display

Quotables Answer: I'm leaving with Weird Al!
— *The One After Joey and Rachel Kiss*

Season 9: Difficult
1. So Cheesy, Slim Pickings and Whole Hog
2. Olivia
3. Theodore and Bitsy
4. Leasing him a Ford Focus
5. Ida Green
6. Kori Weston
7. Unscented oven cleaner
8. St. Mark's Comics
9. Nude pictures of Anna Kournikova
10. A bottle of Merlot and a 5-year-old condom

Quotables Answer: I want you there with your fossil brush!
— *The One with Rachel's Other Sister*

Ross and Joey
1. Powder and lotion
2. The green pillar at Central Perk
3. Joey uses the pipe holding the door open as a telescope
4. People in white coats and people in blue blazers
5. Writing a screenplay
6. Nacho Chair
7. The white dog (Pat)
8. Rossel and Rosstepher
9. His sandwich
10. Kristen Lang

Quotables Answer: The sky's blue, Ross, and I had sex yesterday!
— *The One with the Videotape*

Season 10: Difficult
1. Alicia May Emory
2. A naked dance with scarves
3. Christie Brinkley and C3PO
4. Amanda Buffamonteezi
5. Al Zebooker
6. A napkin with Janice's phone number on it
7. An aquarium and a sex swing
8. Bacon and heavy cream
9. Honesty and a gentle spanking once in a while
10. Phoebe, Monica, Chandler and Joey

Quotables Answer: I forgot to pick up my dry cleaning!
— *The One with Rachel's Going Away Party*

Phoebe's Flings
1. Health inspector
2. Rattle a headboard like a sailor on leave
3. Robert
4. Hums While He Pees
5. Roger
6. Malcolm
7. Phil Huntley
8. Kenny the Copy Guy
9. He's too clingy
10. Brooklyn Heights

Quotables Answer: We're gonna have sex in a public rest room.
— *The One Where Rachel's Sister Babysits*

Expert Quiz 1
1. 495 Grove Street
2. Angela Featherstone
3. Patrick and Eldad
4. 5639
5. 5
6. Porcelain Safari, I Love Lucite, Isn't It Chromantic?
7. 421
8. Photo 152
9. Black 15
10. May 15, 2001

Quotables Answer: I had some money, or a place to go.
— *The One with the Hypnosis Tape*

Expert Quiz 2
1. The One with Mac and C.H.E.E.S.E, The One with the Vows, The One with Joey's Interview, The One with Christmas in Tulsa, and The One Where Chandler Gets Caught
2. Wallace Pincer
3. Lei-lana-lukus
4. A green-blue '95 Buick LeSabre
5. Hugo Lindgren's ring design
6. Mrs. Catrokis
7. 5 Morton Street, Apartment 14
8. 517
9. Snaro
10. Sept. 22, 1994

Quotables Answer: Make the cast of "Cats" sing "Happy Birthday" to me.
— *The One with the Ballroom Dancing*

Expert Quiz 3
1. Stage 24
2. Hosenstein
3. Harmon Killebrew
4. Ashley and Brittany
5. Mittens, Fitzhugh and Jinkys
6. 1202
7. Jon Haugen
8. Aunt Mary; John, her mailman; and Albino Bob
9. 7
10. Ice cubes, aloe vera and a gentle, self-loathing touch

Quotables Answer: Use them in your theater of cruelty.
— *The One with the Candy Hearts*

About the author

Kylie Digges is a lifelong trivia fanatic and the founder of Brainwave Trivia.

A journalism graduate, she has worked as a copy editor, reporter and web producer. This is her first book.

She lives in Mesa, Arizona, with her husband, Tim, and two cats, Djackson and Archer.

Made in the USA
Middletown, DE
22 November 2019

79211521R00102